Praise for

"Millions of adults (therapists, professional helpers, caregivers, family members, etc.) must actively embrace self-care and attune to their own needs in order to be fully present for others. Bravo to the re-publication of *Stillpoint* and kudos to all caregivers!"

–Ilana Rubenfeld, Founder of the Rubenfeld Synergy
Method and author of *The Listening Hand: Self-Healing
Through The Rubenfeld Synergy Method of Talk and Touch*

"Healthcare professionals are facing a self-care crisis; burnout, compassion fatigue, addiction, and suicide are on the rise. In *Stillpoint,* Sheila and Christine have laid out a clear path to healing, allowing people to reclaim their right to self-care. My research in self-compassion has taught me that how we relate to ourselves is critical to our well-being as caregivers. I'm glad to see the latest research being put into a form that is a joy to implement."

–Cynthia Phelps, PhD, entrepreneur, founder, InnerAllies, LLC

"Having worked for over fifty years with hundreds of women as they have provided care for family members, I value this book. With so many demands upon families these day, as parents live longer and need care, as childcare expenses increase, and as concerns for our troubled communities and our planet escalate, *Stillpoint* is needed and helpful. It offers practical and spiritual ways to take care of ourselves so that we may thrive and live to continue to serve life well and joyfully."

–Glenda Taylor, Minister, Founder and Director
of the Fellowship of Comparative Religion

"A powerful, practical "Playbill" of micro self-care practices, ready to apply in any caregiver situation. *Stillpoint* should be required reading for those in the field and for those considering entering it. Each "ACT" identifies easy to incorporate moments and practices of holding, nurturing, grounding, and invigorating throughout one's day and one's career. Organic in its delivery and message, the book flows freely, respectful of the diversity in caregiver settings. *Stillpoint* will change the game for those serving others by holding space and time to be with, and make room for, self."

–Michelle Ramos, Executive Director, Alternate Roots
'Where Arts and Activism Meet'

Stillpoint

SECOND EDITION

A Self-Care Playbook for Caregivers to Find Ease
and Time to Breathe, and Reclaim Joy

Stillpoint

SECOND EDITION

SHEILA K. COLLINS, PHD
CHRISTINE GAUTREAUX, MSW

Cover art, *The Path of Balance*, by Mara Friedman, www.newmoonvisions.com
Interior illustrations by Joe Gautreaux
Cover and Interior Design by Christy Collins, Constellation Book Services

First edition: 2018
16 17 18 19 20 10 9 8 7 6 5 4 3 2 1

Publisher's Cataloging-in-Publication data
Names: Collins, Sheila K., author | Gautreaux, Christine, author.
Title: Stillpoint : a self-care playbook for caregivers to find ease , and time to breathe , and reclaim joy , 2nd edition / Sheila K. Collins, PhD ; Christine Gautreaux, MSW.
Description: Includes bibliographical references and index. | Pittsburgh, PA: Earth Springs Press, 2018.
Identifiers: ISBN 978-1-7323704-0-1 (pbk.) | 978-1-7323704-108 (ebook)
Subjects: LCSH Aging parents--Care. | Adult children of aging parents--Family relationships. | Caregivers--Psychology. | Caregivers--Family relationships. | Caregivers--Mental health. | Self-care, Health. | BISAC FAMILY & RELATIONSHIPS / Parenting / Parent & Adult Child | SELF-HELP / General
Classification: LCC HQ1063.6 C65 2018 | DDC 646.7/8--dc23

Library of Congress Control Number: 2018951306

PERMISSIONS

Poems by Ralph Caplan copyright Herman Miller. Used by permission of Ralph Caplan and Herman Miller.

Excerpt from "The Art of Conscious Celebration: A New Concept for Today's Leaders," by Cathy DeForest copyright 1985, in *Transforming Leadership: From Vision to Results*, John Adams, editor, Miles River Press, Alexandria, VA. Copyright 1986. Reprinted by permission of Miles River Press.

Excerpt from "Burnt Norton" in *Four Quartets*, copyright 1943 by T.S. Eliot and renewed 1971 by Esme Valerie Eliot, reprinted by permission of Harcourt Brace Jovanovich, Inc.

Reprinted from *Black Elk Speaks*, by John G. Neihardt, by permission of University of Nebraska Press. Copyright 1932, 1959, 1972, by John G. Neihardt. Copyright 1961 by the John G. Neihardt Trust.

Song "Let There Be Peace on Earth," copyright 1955 by Jan-Lee Music, renewed 1983. Used by permission of Jill Jackson Miller, Jan-Lee Music.

*To our teachers, students,
mentors, and midwives,
our clients, family members
and dance instructors –
this book is dedicated.*

Playbill

Overture,
Revised Second Edition

I'd lost touch in recent years with the original *Stillpoint* book. It's been nearly 25 years since the book was first published, and, though it hasn't made any bestseller lists, readers throughout the years have told me how meaningful it has been to them. Some have said that they keep it on hand to refer to when the going gets tough, when they are trying to take care of themselves while taking care of others. It turns out that caregiving has been a frequent job, both professionally and informally, throughout the lives of many readers of the first edition, including this author.

If we look at what's changed in our culture since the first edition, it's important to note the staggering reality that more than 65 million people in the United States are now informal caregivers to an elderly or disabled relative or friend. Of caregivers, 66 percent are women, and 17 percent of the American workforce has the additional full- or part-time job of caring for a loved one.[1] Studies indicate that caregiving impacts the caregiver's immune system for up to three years afterwards, making the caregiver more susceptible to developing chronic disease.[2]

Studies using Maslach's burnout scale with workers in the healthcare industry demonstrate that people who do caring work professionally, such as social workers, still experience emotional exhaustion, depersonalization, and reduced feelings of accomplishment more often than those in the general population.[3] The fact that teachers and human service workers in many states are eligible for food stamps demonstrates that appreciation for these workers has not gone up in the form of paying a living wage for these highly trained and dedicated workers.[4]

Having spent five years learning, practicing, and writing about self-care for caregivers came in handy for me when, a year after *Stillpoint* was published, my youngest son, Kenneth, was diagnosed with AIDS. I walked that journey with him, becoming a member, with his two dads, of his caregiving team for three and a half years, till the end of his life. Five years later, my daughter Corinne was diagnosed with breast cancer. She called on me to help with her three young children. Later, I became her 24/7 caregiver for three months when we moved to Houston for her to undergo a bone marrow transplant at M. D. Anderson Cancer Center. A few days before her death, I used my social work skills to help her and her children say goodbye.

After so many experiences accompanying loved ones as they dealt with illness and faced death, I dedicated myself to writing about what I had learned in what became an award-winning memoir, *Warrior Mother: Fierce Love, Unbearable Loss and Rituals that Heal.*[5]

It was friends and colleagues who urged me to revise *Stillpoint* and make it available to a new generation. Following this advice I began working on the revision, but it didn't seem an especially pleasant task until I asked my dear friend and sister colleague Christine Gautreaux to join me as coauthor. Then, as if by magic, everything felt new again and I began remembering how important this information was for me when I wrote it. I'm grateful again to everyone who helped me create the book in the first place and for those on the current revision team.

Media specialists suggested a change in the subtitle since the original, *The Dance of Self-caring, Self-healing,* did not contain any online search terms. It was also suggested that the term "dance" might be misleading. For many people the word "dance" conjures up images of skinny ballerinas or a small child in a swirly skirt—not even close to what I have in mind.

When I refer to self-caring and self-healing and the actions taken for that purpose as a dance, I mean that they need to be done more as an art form than an exercise regime, more as a performance ritual than a set of extra items added to an already overwhelming "to do" list. The new subtitle—*A Self-Care Playbook for Caregivers to Find Ease and Time to Breathe, and Reclaim Joy*—spells out what happens when actions for self-caring and self-healing are done as a dance.

We retained the word "stillpoint" from the original title because that is what makes this book about self-care different from all others. The approach was, and still is, centered in a developing and continuing attention to our somatic selves, a concept familiar to dance and movement therapists. The somatic self is the body as perceived from within.

The word "stillpoint" became attached to the book originally when a group of us involved in the book's production were jostling with one another over the book's title. We borrowed a practice from the Quakers and went into silence together at my dining room table. After a few moments, from what I now know to be their stillpoint, someone in the group said the word "stillpoint." In that moment, everyone at the table agreed that this was the right word that brought everything together. Now, after years in the practice of InterPlay[6], an improvisational creative approach to unlocking the wisdom of the body, created by Cynthia Winton Henry and Phil Porter, I know the *stillpoint* as the creative place in our center, where all that we know is available to us and where the new comes from. In InterPlay we step onto the magic spot in the game, not knowing what we'll say in our three-sentence story about the assigned word or theme, and what emerges surprises us. That's how we know we're there.

Many advances have been made in the fields of health, mental health, neuroscience, and trauma studies relative to what caregivers need to be self-caring and self-healing. In addition to the improvisational tools of InterPlay, we've included updated definitions of mindfulness, as in Jamie McHugh's Embodied Mindfulness, which is informed by traditions centered on the wisdom of the moving body.

We've referenced Kristin Neff's work[7] in the new field of Self-Compassion, which is particularly relevant to self-care for people whose life and work center on having compassion for others. Concepts from the theory of resilience[8] are particularly helpful to people involved in the hazardous work of caregiving. To become stronger rather than weakened by our challenges, which is the definition of resilience, we must recognize the power of mindset (*it matters what we say to ourselves*). To overcome our wired-in negativity bias, we must develop optimism to insure that we grow from our challenges, achieving post-traumatic growth rather than the more familiar outcome of post-traumatic stress (PTSD).

> **Christine:** It's entirely fitting that I have gone on this revision journey with Sheila, because *Stillpoint* is how we met over 20 years ago. I stood in line at a Texas National Association of Social Workers State Conference, where Sheila was a keynote speaker, to get her autograph on my copy of the book. I teasingly remind her that, because I was a student, the cost of the book was my grocery money for the week. A month later, when I attended a women's retreat in the Piney Woods of East Texas, I was surprised and a bit shocked to find Sheila there.
>
> Since then, in addition to Glenda Taylor's retreat group, we have come together often through InterPlay, reconnecting to our bodies' wisdom and to each other, reclaiming the art-based birthright practices of dance, song, storytelling, and stillness. The rest has become our shared herstory.
>
> We're excited to have you join us as you become more committed to, and skilled, at taking care of yourself, in and out of your caregiver roles. ❀

Sheila K. Collins
Christine Gautreaux

Overture (original)

It is said that we teach what we want to learn, and this seemed true as I set out on what has turned out to be a long journey to write this book about self-care. I believe now that the journey has been longer than I expected because I knew even less than I thought I did about self-care and how to be self-caring. And I certainly didn't know that doing something in a self-caring way would take so much longer.

Along the way in this "play within a play," as I attempted to use the book to develop my own self-care skills, I was met by challenging difficulties. In order to arrange time on my calendar for writing I needed to confront an old habit, organizing my life around the convenience of other people. I found it painfully difficult at times to tell clients, colleagues, and family members that I wouldn't be available when they wanted to see me.

Most of the people in my life stayed connected to me through the long book-writing process. But I lost some relationships when I stopped playing by other people's rules. I learned the connection between self-caring and self-healing when I sat down to write. Tuning in to myself in a self-caring way to work on the book, I discovered my exhaustion. I realized I was overworking in order to get time to write. Then, before I could go forward in the preventive way of self-caring, I had to back up and recover, caring enough about myself to do the hard work necessary for self-healing.

I came to believe that the means used to achieve the book would be reflected in the book's final form. I felt, too, that the way I treated myself in the process would be a true measure of what I had learned. As I prepare to let go of these, by now, well-worn pages, it is my hope that you, the reader, will use them gently, as an inspiration for your own self-discovery and recovery.

Prologue

Caring for others is a hazardous occupation. Whether we work in a so-called "helping profession," hold a job in the human service industry providing services to the public, or focus our caregiving on family and friends—the problem is the same. Those of us who care for others have trouble caring for ourselves.

People Who Do Caring Work

In these days of computer technologists, financial planners, and wizards of leveraged buyouts and expansion, there is, in the workplace as well as in the home place, a group of workers dedicated to jobs that involve caring for others. Their number still grows as their contributions continue to be overlooked in the larger societal conversation. In the 1990s *Newsweek* declared, "Greed Is Dead," which turned out to be more than a bit premature. Now, with the increasing aging of the populations in most Western countries, and the rise of chronic diseases such as Alzheimer's and other dementias, more people are needed for the job of serving and caring for others.

In deep appreciation of the important contribution these caregivers make to the well-being of our world, we have elected to revise and re-release this book as a tribute to people working as *caregivers*, professionally and/or informally in their families. We honor these givers that care and hope this book can be a companion on what is often an extended and challenging journey.

Traditionally, caregivers have been found in homes, schools, hospitals, and service organizations, in both salaried and volunteer positions. And they have most often been female. However, recent changes in the economy and other factors mean the number of male caregivers has increased. The growing recognition of the caregivers' need and responsibility to give care to themselves has not materialized as we had hoped in the first edition of *Stillpoint*. It continues to be critical for caregivers, in order to preserve themselves as people capable of caring, to develop and exercise the skills of self-care and self-healing.

As a social work professor, I saw myself in my students and colleagues. We worked enthusiastically helping and serving others. We continued caring for families and friends in our personal lives. But before long, rather than being people who had it all, we seemed more like people who do it all, with little left for ourselves.

Christine and I noticed that the same was true of the clients who have come to us for therapy or coaching through the years. Many are strong, generous people who have hurt themselves in the process of caring for others. They have taken care of family, friends, work, and community projects. It takes a few sessions before they start asking the question, "When is it my turn?" When we suggest that now is the best time to begin using some of their caring energy for themselves, they respond with blank expressions and admit, "I don't have the slightest idea how to do that."

What Is the Situation?

As R. D. Laing, the iconoclastic British psychiatrist, said, "Nobody in the situation knows what the situation is."[1] It's difficult to understand why self-care is so hard to do since we mention it to one another at practically every meeting. "Now, take care of yourself," a mother says to her grown daughter on their parting. "You take care now, you hear," one friend signals to another from across the street. It seems we're constantly making each other promise to take care of ourselves, reminding each other of the importance of self-care almost as often as we say good-bye. In spite of these frequent reminders, we seem unaware of what the situation is, of what we are really up against.

Not knowing how to be self-caring, we caregivers frequently injure ourselves. Christina Maslach reported on her extensive research with nurses, teachers, social workers, police, and others in a book she titled *Burnout: The Cost of Caring*.[2] The burnout Maslach documented amounts to emotional and physical overload leading to exhaustion. People suffering from burnout protect themselves by becoming detached, shutting down emotionally. Many report having feelings of wanting to be left alone and then feeling guilty for having such feelings. For some, a reduced sense of accomplishment occurs as they "go through the motions" without a real caring commitment. Others drop out of careers and relationships that they have invested years in building.

This condition is also known as compassion fatigue, or secondary traumatic stress disorder.[3] It has been documented in nurses, especially those dealing with emergency situations, in hospice workers and other mental and physical health care professionals, and in family members caring for someone with a chronic disease. From what is known about this type of stress, it is clear that strong, healthy people are vulnerable. Whether in our work or in our family lives, when we don't take care of ourselves we lose the ability to continue our lifestyle of caring connection to others.

What makes self-care so hard? How do we get so far off base that we need to take time out from our lives for recovery and healing? If we know how to care for others—children and jobs, friends and good causes—what gets in the way of our including ourselves in all that caring energy?

Prior Injuries

One of the first problems in taking care of ourselves is what we have done to our bodies and what most people around us have done to theirs. After we deny, ignore, or perhaps even abuse our bodies, the distorted feedback we get interferes with our taking care of ourselves properly. Self-healing then becomes a prerequisite to self-caring, and self-caring becomes a way to identify one's need to heal.

The roots of our disregard for ourselves run deep and wide. Caregiving historically has been women's work, and our masculine-focused tradition has devalued both women and the caring service they have provided. "I'm only a housewife or stay-at-home mom" says as much about the culture as it does about the woman who describes herself in those terms.[4] Whether male or female, many of us who do caring work as adults grew up playing the caretaking role in our families. In that situation, self-caring meant taking care of the adults in our lives so they would be able to take care of us. We developed the habit of attempting to earn love by being good and doing good. Afraid to be called "selfish," we became "codependent," caring more for the people in a relationship, or for the relationship itself, than we cared for ourselves.[5] It is easy to confuse self-caring with being selfish. This sets the stage for overdoing our caring role, and we become codependent workaholics, damaging ourselves as we serve others.

Becoming Self-Caring

In order to become self-caring we must first reclaim and recondition our physical selves. We must rediscover our most neglected senses, our movement (kinesthetic) and touch (tactile) senses. These senses contain the information about how we are and what we need. In order to become self-caring we must become receptive to inner signals and give greater credence to our felt experience.

A cultural habit of ignoring the intuitive, feminine way of knowing has us seeking perfection, operating from the abstract and theoretical while losing touch with ourselves and our human needs. Including the feminine in our lives means that both men and women can seek completeness rather than perfection. Incorporating the intuitive feminine with the analytical masculine allows a creative synthesis. Then, we can give attention to the context in which all this occurs. Including the feminine gives us access to a caring ethic[6] that holds an important key to our self-caring. Caring means being able to be receptive to the needs of others, to relate and respond to others and to the needs of the situation. But the feminine principle is inclusive, and it includes the needs of the caregiver as well.

Creative expression is a central human need often overlooked by those of us who care for others. Hans Selye,[7] the researcher who first identified stress, recommended creative expression of our real selves as the key to managing the stress of life. Viewing our life and work as continual opportunities to express ourselves creatively insures that we not bog down in routine, become overwhelmed by criticism, or take ourselves too seriously.

AUTHOR REFLECTIONS

Sheila: As I involved myself as a teacher and therapist in learning and teaching about self-care, I found myself drawing on my background as a dancer. Dancing has been a significant part of my life since childhood. I always knew that dancing was a way for me to take care of myself. As one of my dance teachers used to say, "Dancing doesn't take energy, it makes energy!" I didn't understand the reasons dancing worked in this way, but even my own children, when they were young, noticed the connection between dancing and my ability to cope. When they saw me losing patience with them, they would suggest, "Time for you to go to your dancing class, Mom!"

After a career as a dancer I entered the academic world, where I was continually sensitive to the gaps and omissions in what was officially considered knowledge. Later, as a professor, I was criticized for my inclusion of physical aspects of the self in social work courses. My methods were labeled "touchy-feely" and were considered offensive—a threat to true intellectual pursuit. I felt a bit like the child in the fairy tale "The Emperor's New Clothes," who informed the emperor of his nakedness, an obvious truth no one wanted to hear. In my case, I seemed to be continually reminding people of truths they were trying to forget, namely that there were physical bodies beneath those academic robes.

As a dancer, I have tremendous respect for the importance of technique. Technique builds the strength and skill to perform a great variety of movements while relating to other dancers and the audience. But a dancer's technique is only a vehicle for the creative expression of human experience, including personal, emotional, and communal realities. The dance of caring work is more than techniques, more than action steps. There are movements in which one expresses oneself, and pauses, and transitions of relating and responding to another. Most of all there is, for the caregiver as for the dancer, the use of one's physical self as the stuff of which the dance is made. �به

Christine: Trained as a master social worker, but an athlete since childhood, I struggled with the body piece being left out of traditional counseling classes and workshops. I have been a seeker of self-care techniques and modalities since college. When I discovered InterPlay,[8] thanks to Sheila, all the pieces clicked into place for me. The use of movement, storytelling, and voice added a dimension that was lacking. ✖

Body/Mind Connection

AUTHOR REFLECTIONS

Sheila: This book approaches self-caring and self-healing from the perspective of our psychobiology. Scientists are learning more each day about the effects of mental attitudes, emotions, and personality habits on body functioning. As Bernie Siegel demonstrates in *Love, Medicine and Miracles*,[9] when patients begin dealing with mental, emotional, and spiritual aspects of themselves, their recovery from serious illness is greatly enhanced. This book focuses on the other side of that two-way reciprocal connection: ways to change the body in order to affect our mental, emotional, and spiritual dimensions. The reciprocal communication that begins with the body is less familiar to most people than is the other way around. It took a Shakespearean actor, F. M. Alexander, to discover that a physical symptom, laryngitis, could be caused by incorrect posture and what he called "the misuse of the self."[10] Another contributor to information about our psychophysical nature is Moshe Feldenkrais, an Israeli physicist. Feldenkrais set out to heal himself from a karate injury and wound up mapping the central nervous system. He discovered that when one engages in nonhabitual movements done passively or slowly in a state of relaxation, the brain is stimulated and the mind and body become more flexible.[11] Ilana Rubenfeld, as a music conductor, developed chronic pain in her shoulder. In the search for her own healing, she became a teacher of the Alexander Technique (a system of body reeducation) and a student of both Fritz Perls (father of gestalt therapy) and Moshe Feldenkrais (master of movement education). Rubenfeld created a body-oriented psychotherapy, the Rubenfeld Synergy Method,[12] a synthesis of these methods. She added music, hypnosis, and her own artistic expression of humor. While I was her student, her strong emphasis on self-care sparked my interest in writing about self-caring and self-healing. Building on the work of these illustrious pioneers and manifested in the expression that is this book, I offer my experiences as a dancer, social worker, and teacher to caregivers, both professional and informal, on behalf of their own self-care and self-healing. ❊

Christine: In the last 20 years, we have discovered more about how the brain and the body talk to each other, which has led to new techniques and methods that work hand in hand with traditional ones. EMDR (eye movement desensitization and reprocessing) is an evidenced-based system that enables people to heal from the symptoms and emotional distress that are the result of disturbing life experiences. Repeated studies show that by using EMDR therapy, people can experience the benefits of psychotherapy that once took years to make a difference.[13] Another favorite of mine is tapping. This technique requires the person to focus on a negative emotion or unresolved problem while using their fingertips to tap 5–7 times on each of 12 of the body's meridian points, restoring their body's energy to a balanced state.[14] I love how accessible this technique and others have become, but as I work with people currently, I find that important principles and concepts presented in this book, such as codependency or somatic practices, are unfamiliar to them. I'm grateful that this revision of *Stillpoint* can bring together the new with the tried and true, in one place. ❋

The Benefits

As you learn more about your psychophysical self and the steps in the dance of self-caring/self-healing you will

- find and communicate with the parts of yourself that need your caring (Self- Compassion);
- identify the elements missing in your self-caring lifestyle;
- increase your understanding of yourself as a strong yet vulnerable living system;
- learn ways to recondition your body's response to threat and find ease in the midst of challenge;
- learn self-care skills to take time to breathe as you care for yourself while you are caring for others in your life;
- learn to alter your work environment to support self-care for yourself and the other people who spend time there;
- discover the use of creative expressions such as movement, music, and dance to release tension and generate positive energy and reclaim joy;
- explore humor as a tool of creative expression, to defuse or reframe difficult situations; and

- apply your creative and artistic talents in making your own healing rituals following the model provided.

Guide to Using This Book

Self-caring and self-healing require moving beyond our logical, intellectual minds into the kinesthetic, feminine, and creative parts of ourselves. Throughout this book, you will encounter these three terms representing aspects of ourselves. The *kinesthetic* senses put us in touch with our body's wisdom, giving us information about ourselves and the world around us. In Western culture animals and young children are better at relying on these senses than are adults, whose intellectual education has stifled many adults' ability to use them. The term *feminine* refers to the cluster of human qualities and abilities that exist in both men and women but which have been historically assigned to women. Self-care and self-healing for both men and women requires respecting and reclaiming these important human qualities. We explore *creativity* because many adults in our culture have become convinced that without special talent or expert training they cannot consider themselves creative, or exercise this aspect of themselves.

This book is organized so as to encourage you, the reader, to explore and learn from your own, as well as other people's, experiences.

Since stories are a powerful way to learn what can be, at times, mysterious principles, I have constructed stories from the experiences of many people I have worked with these past twenty years. To protect their privacy we have altered identifying information and sometimes combined experiences of more than one person into a single story. It is my hope that you will recognize yourself, as I did, in the people and situations illustrated.

Act One defines self-care and its connection to self-healing. We meet a pair of fanciful characters who help us better understand the scientific information about how our bodies and minds work together. Five self-caring skills are introduced through a retelling of the myth of Psyche, and caregivers tell their stories and describe difficulties in taking care of themselves.

Act Two focuses on self-care and self-healing in the two major settings of our lives, our work and our home. We explore the workplace, ways to work in a self-caring way when relating in large scale organizations, and how to become self-caring in your own home environment.

Act Three of the book deals with the practice and rehearsal of self-care and self-healing skills in the four dimensions: physical, mental, emotional, and spiritual. We work with each dimension individually while recognizing in song and story that self-care and self-healing require continuous integration of all four dimensions.

Act Four includes directions for designing your own self-caring lifestyle and healing rituals. The appendixes contain a sample ritual as well as Movements for Mending, references, and resource guides. Throughout the book you will find poems, songs, and stories along with, at times, a lighthearted spirit of humor. Not intended as irreverence to the importance of the topic, an attitude of play is used to sustain us through what can be a hazardous dance. This book is called a "playbook" to suggest that work on your own self-care needs to be done in a playful spirit and in short segments of time. Give yourself permission after reading a section to put the book aside and let your inner creativity make connections to your life situations.

You will find exercises and suggestions for steps to take on behalf of your own self-care and self-healing. Experimenting with taking action will help you get the most out of the book. Other items can become ongoing parts of your daily self-caring lifestyle. In any case, you will find your willingness to take action and use your own body's wisdom to be the most powerful tool in creating your own learning.

Remember the Chinese proverb:

I hear, and I forget;
I see, and I remember;
I do, and I understand.

Act One

Steps, Techniques, and Essential Elements

In order to perform the dance of self-care/self-healing, caregivers must learn many steps, and develop and practice many techniques. Unfortunately, our early training (both personal and professional) prepared us only to do the movements of caregiving for others, without regard for ourselves. This means, in order to meet our needs as caregiving adults, we are faced with the task of unlearning habits and changing our mindset.

Most of our teachers and role models did not take care of themselves, so they could not teach us the dance of self-care. They may have spoken of its value, but to become a dancer one must dance. To learn the steps, one observes and copies people who have the routine in their bodies, in their bones. And mostly, one needs permission to perform the ordinary movements of everyday life in such a way that they won't interfere with self-caring and result in setting up the need for self-healing.

The first two chapters of this book look at the change in our attitude towards taking care of ourselves that is necessary to perform caregiving as a healthy and graceful dance. In the resilience literature, this is known as mindset. We note the connection between the dance of self-care and self-healing and how, when you perform self-care more often, you have less need for self-healing. Caregivers tell their own stories of how they often injured themselves as they performed their caregiving work. We identify the essential self-care elements and offer you, the reader, a way to identify which essential elements may be missing in your life.

The Material for the dance is air,
the movement is breath,
and the source is love.
–Fran Levy, Dance Therapist

Becoming a Self-Caring, Self-Healing Person

Love thyself as thy neighbor.

Moshe Feldenkrais, *The Potent Self*

- Are you a person who takes care of others and has trouble asking for (or knowing) what you need for yourself?
- Do you treasure relationships, often putting up with people's lack of consideration for you?
- Do you often find, as you make and complete your "to do" list, that your needs are not even on your list?
- Do you dream of a world where all people will flourish?
- Do you feel uncomfortable (have trouble flourishing) when anyone you love is unhappy or in trouble?
- Are you a person who stays too long in a job or in a relationship out of a sense of loyalty, forgetting about the loyalty you owe to yourself?
- Do you go courageously to the front lines to tend the sick, wounded, and needy?
- Do you dream up projects to tend to the needs of the sick, wounded, and needy, and then get *blamed* as though you dreamed up the sick, wounded, and needy?

If you have answered yes to three or more of these questions, you are in need of learning the skills of self-care and self-healing. In addition, you will probably need a lot of encouragement to put self-care into the center of your daily life. So find two or three friends and ask them these same questions. If they answer the same way you did, they are likely candidates to go on this journey of recovery with you. (We will go into more detail later on the importance of *Partnership Power*.) In teaching professional helpers, I have encountered many people who would answer "yes" to most of the above questions. And even without asking, by scanning the facial expressions and body postures of the students before me, I could often guess how far they have strayed from self-care. Hunched shoulders, hyperextended necks, eyes straining to see as though through a thick fog, all testify to the effort and struggle that life has become. Sometimes the students' self-carelessness has amounted to a small miscalculation of limits and vulnerabilities or to an underestimation of what a particular project will require. Like the cafeteria diner whose 'eyes are bigger than their stomach,' we sometimes take on more than any human being could handle comfortably.

Susan, a nurse-practitioner, had been experiencing headaches, tiredness, and a lack of her usual vigor. "Opening the new clinic was exciting, but it turned out to be all-consuming. Adding all the startup tasks on top of my regular workload has meant longer-than-ever work hours and a sense of going in all directions at once."

Other times self-carelessness has gone on far longer, under more intense pressure. Robert, a former counselor, put it this way: "I loved working with the clients in the beginning, but before it was over I wasn't doing them any good—or myself either. By the time I figured out what was happening to me, my burnout had cost me my marriage as well as my health."

So self-care and self-healing are intertwined. Impossible to separate at times, they weave back and forth like grapevines weaving around each other. As we desire to become more self-caring, we discover the effects of prior injuries. As we attempt to heal, we notice our need to take better care of ourselves.

Self-care is a place halfway between selfless and selfish. Between the two extremes of the "saint" whose only regard is for others and the "sinner" who thinks only of her- or himself, self-care is a place for regular people. Rather than taking a position of "them or me," self-care involves an inclusive sense of "and." Self-care means caring for oneself while, at the same time, caring for others.

Self-Care **Is Not**

- Continuing to educate and train ourselves to <u>withstand more stress in order to take on more stress.</u> We all know people who insist on staying in unhealthy jobs or relationships while asking for help in order to tolerate more abuse more gracefully.
- Putting ourselves through frequent recurring cycles of overwork followed by crashing to recover. This rhythm of full speed ahead followed by total collapse is damaging to all dimensions of our selves: the physical, mental, emotional, and spiritual.

Self-Care **Is**

- Tuning in: recognizing, earlier and earlier, the subtle physical signs of potential difficulties. Caring people become good at reading other people's body language: clenched jaw, stooped shoulders, and sad eyes. Self-care means tuning in to ourselves and learning how to *read our own body language.*

Alcoholics don't have to wait to hit bottom on skid row before beginning their recovery. As we tune in earlier and earlier to ourselves and our own needs, we caregivers don't have to hit bottom—*we don't have to get sick in order to get well.*

Self-Care **Is**

- Tending. Being actively involved in a caring role creates the potential for taking on other people's tensions and stress. In tending to ourselves, we perfect the art of not taking on other people's tension. And when we do take on their tension, by tending to ourselves, we learn to let go quickly so that we are free to experience a life of balance and vitality.

AUTHOR REFLECTIONS

Christine: The self-care alternative, like all places of moderation and balance, is not easy to find, develop, and sustain over time. As we grow to become more self-caring, we discover our need to become self-healing as well. When I think of self-healing I flash on the stack of self-care books that used to be piled on the table beside my bed when I was looking for an easy fix. This vision illustrates for me more about what self-healing is not. The process of self-healing involves each of us accessing our own inner-body wisdom and tapping into our individual truth for what our body and soul need. It often includes self-compassion, incremental steps, and being gentle with ourselves. �֍

Self-Healing **Is Not**

- Making unnecessary efforts from a desire to please, from the fear of making a mistake, or through the excess energy of our own enthusiasm. Our lives become graceful dances when we remove these extras and perform according to our own inner rhythm.

- Turning ourselves over to "experts." Whatever knowledge the specialists might have, I am the only *real* expert on me. You are the only *real* expert on you. The self is not only the *object* of the healing but the *agent* of the healing as well. If we don't yet consider ourselves experts on ourselves, we can become so by applying the skills of self-care and self-healing.

Self-Healing **Is**

- Making whole. The place where it hurts may not be the place where the difficulty lies. We could have pain in our shoulder or in our hips, the result of years of walking in poorly fitting shoes. Discovering the message in the pain involves listening to the wisdom of our body, and then letting go of what is unnecessary while supplying the essential missing elements. When you were learning to write your name, it took great effort. It became easier when you learned to eliminate extra movements of your face and tongue and loosen your grip on the pencil. Eventually you easily made your signature legible.

- Unlearning the habits we acquired as we accommodated previous traumas. Recovery from a broken leg doesn't involve just getting the cast off. We must unlearn, or let go, of the way we have been walking to accommodate the cast.

- Transforming the pain in such a way that its truth becomes understandable. Pain is a signal that something is wrong. Discovering the message in the pain involves listening to the wisdom of our bodies and taking steps to change the circumstances that have created the pain.

- Correcting imbalances whether in diet, body posture, work, or family. A lot of what we do to take care of ourselves really doesn't work because we tend to overdo one or two favorite things. Self-care and self-healing involve looking at the whole picture and discovering where omissions and excesses may be, then taking steps to move towards balance.

The Kinesthetic Self

The connection between self-care and self-healing finally occurred to me after many incidents of illness, injury, and recovery. After experiencing nearly total collapse at one of Anna Halprin's dance workshops on self-healing, I realized that if I took better care of myself in the first place, I might not need self-healing so often. Remembering Anna's comment about her own experience with cancer and healing from it—"I must have thought I was indestructible"—reminds me of the power of mindset.

Injury can come from the most unlikely places. After spending many years in the academic environment, with such intense emphasis on one particular way of thinking and experiencing the world and myself, I felt the need to heal. It wasn't just that the logical, intellectual, and objective were emphasized. Most damaging to my spirit was the relentless ridicule of the intuitive, subjective, and felt experience, which was discounted and labeled "touchy-feely."

In order to act on our own behalf, we need to develop sensitivity for reading the external messages in the environment and be able to identify and name our own internal experience as well. Rather than running from the term "touchy-feely," or regarding it as a vague insult, let's realize that these complementary parts of our kinesthetic senses are basic to our being, the stuff of which the dance is made. For the sake of precision and accuracy in our own self-care ability, let's exercise our power to name by using the name Touchy to represent our ability to make contact with the outer world, the world outside our skin. The name Feelie can be used for our subjective inner experience, which helps us connect with our own sensations and emotions. Instead of a vague label with negative connotations, "touchy-feely" can be redefined as positive resources, Touchy and Feelie, to be respected and fine-tuned as we mature.

The Creative Self

What if we had a culture that taught us, as children, to trust our sensory and motor systems, our Touchy and Feelie senses? What if, as adults, we reclaimed our Touchy and Feelie senses and dared to trust our own experience? And how much better could we take care of ourselves if we knew how to communicate with our sensory and motor systems? It is in this spirit, and to these ends, that I offer the following story.

As I was studying and writing about the kinesthetic senses, I remembered twin playmates I had as a child, unseen—but real to me. My parents called them "imaginary" and decided I had invented them because Mother was preoccupied with my new baby brother. But perhaps this was my own creative way of connecting with Touchy and Feelie, of connecting with my own inner self. I hadn't thought of my unseen playmates in years; but last summer, as I was studying and reading everything I could get my hands on about how our bodies, minds, emotions, and spirits function together, I thought of the twins again. As we became reacquainted, it was as though I were rediscovering parts of myself long hidden. Now let me introduce Feelie.

Feelie is highly sensitive and feminine, capable of a powerful inner focus, which she uses at times to close off all other input and distractions. As she goes into her inner still-point, the place where all new thoughts and ideas are birthed, she is able to identify what she is experiencing. This is especially important for her own self-care, in identifying her need for comfort and necessities such as food, water, and sleep. Feelie really knows who she is and where she is at any particular moment. Her special relationship to gravity keeps her well oriented in time and space. If Feelie could speak for herself she would say, "I know up from down and all the other dimensions and directions by responding to my own inner signals. By sensing my internal organs and the experience of inner personal space, I recognize immediately when I'm off balance or when something I'm doing isn't good for me. I experience warmth, cold, pressure, and pain, and I'm especially fond of learning from pleasure."

When I remember Feelie from my childhood, I hear her full-bodied, heartfelt laughter. I love her sense of humor, her laughter at the slightest provocation. I'm reminded of Feelie whenever I hear the squeals and giggles of children or smell the aroma of chocolate chip cookies.

Now let's meet Feelie's twin, Touchy. Touchy is strongly masculine and what you might call a mover and a shaker. He likes charging out into the world, contacting and sensing with his whole body. He learns about mountains by climbing them, not by viewing them from afar.

Touchy is every bit as sensitive as Feelie. He notices pressure, heat, cold, and pain. He laughs a lot and may be even fonder of pleasure than Feelie is. I admire Touchy's range and flexibility. He can move in every direction imaginable. In fact, if you look closely, you might notice the small, subtle movements of his muscles whenever he even pictures moving in his mind's eye.

I see my friend Touchy as really knowing how to make contacts. He takes care of himself by moving out, using his own brand of detective skills to discover what's out there and what's needed to ebb and flow with it.

If Touchy could speak, he'd say, "Most people don't realize that both Feelie and I process and organize a tremendous amount of information. Feelie is sensory; and I am motor; all stimulation of doing, learning, remembering, and healing are ordered by us, the sensory and motor systems."

As we learn to reconnect with our own twins (our sensory and motor systems), we learn we can trust them with our very lives. I called on Touchy and Feelie, the Soma Twins[1] for some background on how our misunderstandings about these senses have developed.

"Down through the ages we have been mistreated," said Touchy, "and the senses we represent relegated to a less important position than they deserve. We have been called evil, foolish, or the work of the devil at times, while at other times, we have been totally ignored. In Western culture, we seem to get lost altogether for long periods of time."[2]

Feelie added, "The recent widespread practice of using drugs has been a source of concern, since people seem to think that is the way to get in touch with us."[3]

Responding to Feelie, I said, "Years ago, one of the most misunderstood messages was the rallying cry for the faithful of a California cult: 'Experience ecstasy! Lose your mind and come to your senses!' Can you clarify this for us now?"

Both of the twins nodded at once, and Touchy said, "*Stop leading with your logical mind. The logical part is designed to follow the body's sensing, feeling parts.*" I thought of my ballroom dancing teacher, Eddie. He's always telling me, "Don't think, just follow!" And another dancing teacher gave this advice: "When spinning around, do not focus on the outer, moving edges. Stay in the place in the center that is not moving, the *stillpoint.* You'll be able to perform multiple turns at high speed without getting dizzy." This suggests the possibility that you may contact your sensory and motor systems and, like the whirling dervishes, experience ecstasy without chemicals.

"At the very least," Touchy teased, "you will open up your sinus cavities, which is probably a prerequisite to experiencing ecstasy in any culture!"

On that note we leave Touchy and Feelie, my Soma Twins, knowing that we can call on them again to help us understand how they function, separately and together, to aid our self-care and self-healing.

The Feminine Self

In all cultures and times, women have performed the dance of caregiving, feeding and caring for themselves in order to feed and care for their young. This dance, ancient and natural, has not been an easy one. Folk stories and myths have spelled out the difficulties of this continuing human dilemma—caring for oneself while caregiving for another.

Steps in the dance of self-care are described in Greek mythology, in the tale of Psyche. According to the story, in order to be reunited with her husband, from whom she had become separated, Psyche had to master several skills. She had to develop her own identity, learn how to get what she needed from an unfriendly world, ask for help for herself, and put limits on her helping of others. Psyche was given four tasks to complete. These tasks illustrate the five skills of self-care. These skills help us build and maintain strong boundaries between ourselves and those we care about, so that we don't lose ourselves in the process.

The Five Skills of Self-Care

1. *Sorting and Separating* what belongs to us from what belongs to others
2. *Letting Go and Surrendering* and learning when and how to do this
3. *Building and Using Partnership Power* to get help from others
4. *Stepping Back* to see the big picture and the relationship between parts
5. *Exercising Choice* by saying No and Yes

Let's retell the ancient Psyche tale with its archetypical view of the feminine helping role. We will look at each of Psyche's four tasks, followed by the five self-care skills that are illustrated. In addition, we will examine a contemporary situation in which each skill can be useful.

Self-Care Skills and the Myth of Psyche

Meet Psyche, the pregnant mortal wife of the god Eros and daughter-in-law of none other than Aphrodite, goddess of love. As you can see from her illustrious relatives, this lady hung out in some mean company. Somehow she got separated from her husband just at the time she needed him the most, being pregnant and all. Since she was a mere mortal, she decided to throw herself on the mercy of her mother-in-law, who was a goddess of pretty high rank and a known expert on this loving, caring business.

Why Aphrodite was on the outs with her daughter-in-law isn't clear in the various versions of the story, and it isn't clear why she didn't just use her vast powers to set things right for the young couple. Instead, Aphrodite devised four extremely difficult tasks for Psyche to master before she could be reunited with her husband. As it turned out, these assignments were for Psyche's own good, teaching her the skills needed for self-care in personal, work, and family relationships. As you read about Psyche's struggles, ask yourself if you have developed these essential self-care skills in your own life.

Task One: Sorting the Seeds

In her first task, Psyche was given a large pile of seeds of various types, all mixed together. She was told to separate them into piles according to whether they were oats or beans or barley seeds. Picture this poor woman, sitting at the table shuffling and grouping the seeds into separate piles, singing, "Oats and beans and barley seeds, oats and beans and barley seeds." We can admire her grace in accepting such a meticulous and monotonous task.

Self-Care Skill One: Doing Your Own Sorting Work

In reality, the tasks of *Sorting and Separating* our own seeds can be fascinating, fun, and enlightening. The seeds of our own discontent have been planted in our past, sowed by mother, father, grandparents, even ancestors dead long before our birth. To *sort* out the messages of the past and to separate them from present people and realities means that we can choose which seeds we want to flourish in our own psyche. "One seed is from Mom, this one's from Dad. Don't forget Grandma. She always looked sad."

Contemporary Example: Your Own Sorting Work

Imagine yourself in the following situation. You are having a discussion with a friend, a coworker, or your boss. The outcome is important. The discussion and the person you are speaking with begin to stir old feelings, reminding you of someone else, such as your ex-spouse, his bossy mother, or the boogie man! If you come on like gangbusters, reacting in this situation to feelings left over from another era, you are gonna get yourself in a whole lot of trouble. You will probably blow the deal, lose your friend, or hurt someone you love.

You need to sort out the seeds of the past and separate them from present reality. Imagine you can take two little wires, like brackets [ ], place them around the memory, feeling, or issue that is emerging for you in the present context, and go on with the business at hand.[4] Make a note to deal with this later in a context that is appropriate for sorting the seeds of your own discontent. Keep in mind that unfinished business and unresolved situations drain energy. Ultimately, doing your own psychological and emotional sorting work results in lightening your load. A caring lifestyle becomes easier as you no longer need to carry around the people and situations of the past.

Task Two: Gathering the Golden Fleece

The next task that Aphrodite presented to Psyche was to gather some golden fleece from a herd of mean, aggressive sheep. Now these were not those cute little fuzzy sheep that children cuddle or grownups count as they go off to sleep. We're talking about big bully rams, busy butting heads and locking horns with one another, over who knows what! Turns out, Psyche's no dumbbell. She doesn't even try to wrestle those rams or beat them at their own game. She waits until nightfall, when the rams have gone. Then she gathers the wool that stuck to the bushes where the rams were fighting and feuding with one another during the day!

Self-Care Skill Two: Letting Go and Surrendering

Many of us have given up our caring, helping, intuitive natures when confronted with head-to-head power plays. If you join the bully rams at their game, you lose your own way of being. There's also the risk of acquiring bruises and broken bones when playing war games. If you fight the power-hungry rams or try to talk them out of their anger, you risk starting a stampede that will trample all gentle beings under hoof, including me and you.

Contemporary Example: Letting Go and Surrendering

Suppose you are sitting with a friend who is obstinate, complaining, and difficult. Whatever suggestions you make, your friend responds with "Yes, but . . ." You feel your energy draining from your body and imagine if you don't do something soon, you will need, at the very least, a complete energy transfusion. Rather than continuing these "going nowhere and using your own energy to not get there" movements, try de-escalating by *Letting Go* (it's not going to happen your way, any-how), *Surrendering* to whatever seems possible (go with the flow), and giving up for now, as Psyche did so cleverly when she put things off until nightfall. ("You may be right; there may not be a solution to this situation, at least not right now.")

Task Three: Filling the Flask

In order for Psyche to live a loving life with Eros, she had to fill a crystal flask with waters from a forbidden stream. Not to make this task too easy, the stream was guarded by dragons. The whole thing looked hopeless until Psyche consulted an eagle and together they were able to back off from the scene and get a panoramic perspective. According to the ancient story, our heroine was then carried by the eagle to the stream, down past the dragons, where she filled the flask and they took off airborne before they were discovered.

Self-Care Skill Three: Building and Using Partnership Power[5]

This task demonstrates two self-care skills. Instead of getting caught up with the barriers and becoming overwhelmed by the difficulty of a task, you may link up with others. It's amazing how often those of us who help others forget to ask for help for ourselves.

Self-Care Skill Four: Stepping Back for a Broader Perspective

Stepping Back from a situation and getting a bird's-eye view enables us to note patterns and significant details not obvious when viewed from close up. We can then move in quickly to accomplish what is necessary to sustain our own lives and to protect our significant relationships.

Contemporary Example: Partnership Power and Stepping Back

So here you are, a gentle, fair-minded soul, and some dingbat (parent, colleague, former friend, teenager) is abusing you. They are screaming, name-calling, and blaming you for all the ills of the last millennium. You find yourself shrinking inside. Part of you is in disbelief: "How could they?" Another part is picturing scenes of how you would like to see this person tortured, and still another part is believing what they are saying about you.

As you probably have noticed by now, not everyone operates from your value system of conscientiously helping and caring for others. Taking care of one's gentle soul in the presence of dragons calls for advanced self-care skills. This is especially true when you realize that, as in the myth of Psyche, dragons often guard the flowing waters of what is essential for our survival. In order not to take in the dragon energy and become dragons ourselves, or be run off by the fear of them, we must build strong, confident boundaries.

Self-care skills *Stepping Back* and *Partnership Power* can come to your aid. To back off, imagine you are viewing the scene from a surveillance camera like the ones stores use to catch shoplifters. Or imagine you are viewing the scene through a camera mounted on a drone. Get some assistance from your sense of humor by picturing the scene as a comic strip and the people, including yourself, as cartoon characters. Don't hesitate to call for assistance from passersby, friends, or strangers, and your own Higher Power.

Task Four: Saying No to the Needy

The final and by far the most difficult task given Psyche by Aphrodite was to descend into the underworld. Her assignment was to take a small box to the goddess Persephone and get her to fill it with some kind of beauty ointment. Now this doesn't sound too serious or difficult, but here comes the hard part. This gentle, loving woman is warned that she will be beseeched by pathetic people who will beg and plead for her help. Three times she must have the courage to stay on her own life's journey while people in need are pleading for her to stop and assist them. Should she allow herself to be drawn to help them, she will stay forever in the underworld and never become reunited with her husband.

Self-Care Skill Five: Exercising Choice

In the musical "Oklahoma," when Ado Annie sings Rogers and Hammerstein's song "I'm Just a Girl Who Can't Say No," the audience is amused. But for a person who can't stay on his or her own life's path, the digressions are anything but funny. Saying yes or no must be a win-win situation, for ourselves and for the other person. From the perspective of self-care, we must not say *yes* to another unless, in the same act, we are saying *yes* to ourselves.

Contemporary Example: Exercising Choice

Since setting limits and saying *no* is such a difficult yet necessary skill, let's look at a number of situations where *no* is the kindest answer you can give.

- A close friend wants you to join his church, become president of the PTA, or run away with him to Nigeria. Your own life goals are in another direction, so you say, "Thanks for the compliment, it was good of you to think of me." And "No, that isn't right for me."

- A relative, friend, or neighbor asks you for something and you give it to them. Instead of expressing gratitude she or he criticizes what you have done and immediately thinks up something else for you to do to prove you really care. The only escape from this bottomless pit is to climb out quickly (*Surrender*) and forgive yourself for falling into this pit in the first place. You say, "No, *I'm sorry* you haven't been pleased by my efforts and gifts. I've done all I can."

- Your son, spouse, or dearest friend is dedicated to living a reckless life of self-destruction by riding his or her motorcycle without a helmet, drinking and driving, or continually ingesting illegal or over-the-counter chemicals. As pitiful as this person seems, run, do not walk, to save you own life. Your response: "I wish you all the best, but *I will no longer hurt myself* by watching you hurt yourself."

- A person has needed your care because of age, illness, or a situation of stressful overload. You have said yes to all their requests, and now it is the time when, to rebuild confidence, the person needs to do for her- or himself. You respond, "No, *I won't do it for you*, but I'll support you in doing what you need to do for yourself."

You're probably saying to yourself, "If it were only as easy as it sounds!" To be in touch with one's own experience, to understand and define its meaning, and to act self-caringly on behalf of one's own self, takes discipline and practice, practice, practice!

*He who cannot dance
puts the blame on the floor.*

–Hindi Proverb

2

Caregivers and Their Caring Work

Stories are data with a soul.

–Brene Brown

"There is danger in the telling of the tale," I had been told, but I learned the meaning of this truth the hard way. I was directing my first workshop on self-care for helping professionals. The participants were child welfare workers on society's front line. Their caring work involved investigating complaints of child abuse and neglect—when they weren't filling out paperwork or fighting with the cumbersome state system that employed them.

The Dangers in Caregiving

We began the workshop logically, stating the problems of their caring work. I suggested to the participants: "Think about your work experience, a typical day or week, and about the situations that create for you the greatest difficulty. Perhaps it is a particular time of day when you seem to run out of steam or a situation that continues to repeat itself. 'Here we go again,' you may be saying to yourself. Imagine the type of situation where you feel the most vulnerable in your own self-care, a

21

time when you wind up feeling drained, as though you have lost track of yourself."

"Paperwork is what does me in!" said Donald. "I like the work, being with the clients, but the forms can drown you. The worst day is when I've set aside time to catch up, and an emergency comes along, which has to take precedence. If I hadn't expected to do paperwork that day, it wouldn't have been so bad. But the fact of the matter is, there is no time to do the paperwork that's required in the job. I resent the feeling of this unfinished business hanging over my head and the dull headache I carry for days."

One of the women supervisors chimed in, "There are layers to this. As a supervisor I know the job is often impossible, but if the paperwork isn't done we lose workers. One unit didn't document all of their client contacts and they lost a worker. Central office said they didn't need as many staff."

"I hate being the bad guy and having to say no to clients and staff when we don't have the resources," a Mexican American woman named Norma remarked. "Clients look up to you and expect that you can do anything, when in fact we are very limited."

"The hardest part for me is being the last resort," said Susan, a woman in her late twenties. "I'm the end of the line for the people who come to me. When kids have to be removed from their homes for their protection it's against the law to take them to the jail (the only local facility). The proper facilities are too far away from the rural community where I work. So, late at night and on weekends, they drop them off at my home. This doesn't happen every weekend, but when it does, it means I have no time off from caretaking."

Dottie, a woman in her middle forties, spoke up, "I used to do that, but no more. I used to get so many calls at home; my husband put his foot down. Of course, since his mother came to live with us, I'm back to feeling I never have any time off anyway."

As group members continued complaining and commiserating with one another, sharing "war stories" and situations in which they felt most vulnerable, I felt a dramatic change in the energy in the room. Gone were the pleasant expectations of a day away from the office and the gentle curiosity about the workshop schedule. In their place was a dark discouragement bordering on despair. I imagined a sweatshop of the last century—workers chained to large machines, the cogs of great wheels grinding too slowly in spite of the workers' painful and costly efforts. This image of grinding prompted me to suggest a ten-minute break, for my own sake as well as for the sake of the participants. And then it hit me. In the telling of their tales, workshop participants were reexperiencing their work traumas and frustrations. They were reinfecting themselves and each other with feelings of hopelessness and helplessness about their work situations. No one in the room seemed to be breathing until I called time out.

When we reconvened I shared my "sweatshop fantasy" with the group and, amidst laughter and some nods of recognition, one woman seemed to be speaking for everyone when she made this comment: "It's like what they say about the weather—we all talk about it, but you can't do anything about it. When everybody sits around and bitches at my agency, this makes the problems worse for me. If I'm just left to do my job I'm fine, but it takes me two days to get over a staff meeting. We're called in and told about the pending budget cuts or the new policies, and it comes down to 'do more with less,' and we don't have any say about it anyway."

"How we are when we're together makes a tremendous difference for me in being able to take care of myself," Norma said. "I finally figured out that when I have lunch with a certain group of people (I call them the 'doom and gloom guys'), I have no energy left for the afternoon."

At this point I suggested we all "circle up" (as in "circling the wagons") and join hands. We took a deep breath together and let it out with an audible sigh. I directed the members of the group to each develop an inner focus while staying connected to the person on either side and, through them, to the whole group. I offered the following affirmation:

"I appreciate myself as a precious, valuable person who has chosen to do a difficult and sometimes impossible job. Because I cannot do everything, I take heart in doing what I can do for others and for myself. I remember that I am not alone; others travel this caring path with me. I realize that the caring energy that has motivated us to be in these jobs is sustaining us and helping us to learn whatever is most needed for our self-care and self-healing at this time in our lives."

As the group members listened to my voice, they moved gently in rocking motions, nurturing themselves as one might soothe a distraught infant in the middle of the night. Our joined hands served to allow each person to experience connection with the larger group while staying centered in his or her individual rhythm. The rest of our time together went very differently from the beginning phase. The group meditation and affirmation that we did released us from living in and being overwhelmed by problems.

We began living in and experiencing solutions together. We began identifying the important missing elements in caregivers' lives. By the end of our time together the group members were sharing specific strategies they have used to include elements of self-care in their busy lives.

The Missing Elements

As I have continued to work with professional and informal family caregivers through the years, I've heard many verses of what might be called "The Caregiver's Lament." Not all caregivers have to deal with a large bureaucracy like the child welfare workers I've just described. Not all caregivers deal with life-threatening emergencies on a regular basis as they do. But millions of people, whether professional caregivers or not, have a second job when they come home, providing assistance to ill or disabled parents and elder relatives. And whatever the setting or circumstances, we caregivers face our biggest challenge in finding ways to take care of ourselves.

In living a lifestyle in which caring for others is a central focus, essential elements such as *rest* and *recreation* can be missing. Or there can be an imbalance between two essential elements such as *work* and *play*. When one element is overrepresented in our lives, something else vital to our self-care is being left out.

The child welfare workers, for example, were so caught up in the tremendous responsibility of their jobs and the serious problems in their workplace that there was little sense of humor or true connection with one another. Sometimes there is too much *sound* and not enough *silence*, too much *abstinence* and not enough *nourishment*. And *movement* and *activity*, though vital elements, need to be balanced by opportunities for *stillness*.

As in many aspects of our lives, in our self-care it's possible to have too much of a good thing. Too much solitude may turn into isolation. Too much work means not enough play, resulting in a dull and joyless life in the short run. The long run effect can be burnout, sickness, and even death.

Lament of the Professional Caregivers

Let's listen to some other caregivers chanting their own unique verses of the caregiver's lament. Notice the common themes and how they reverberate with your own experience. As you read their stories, see if you can identify essential elements in the lives of the caregivers (such as work and play, sound and silence) that are out of balance or missing altogether.

"No wonder I'm a workaholic!
My family and social life are in shambles!"

Cynthia is a 43-year-old marriage and family therapist. She has a large, successful practice and supervises and trains other professionals. "I finally got the divorce I should have gotten years ago, and I'm OK about that. It took a lot for me to admit I couldn't save my own marriage when I have been so successful in helping other people to save theirs. But I got past that. The problem now seems to be, how do I develop a whole new personal and social life when I am so involved in my work? I feel I need permission to take time out for myself without getting sick to do it."

Cynthia touches on several themes familiar to many helping professionals. We know, for balance in our lives, a well-rounded social and personal life is critical. But it's often not as easy as it sounds. When the element of *work* is not balanced with *play*, less effective work, and finally illness, results. Being sick is one way to get a guilt-free day off, but it's a lousy way to have to spend it.

Relationship difficulties in our personal and family lives are particularly challenging for those of us whose work involves helping others. Our need to work things out with spouses, children, and friends can go far beyond other people's willingness to invest in that process. And some difficulties occur precisely because of our professional work. When my daughter was an adolescent she found a clever way to discount me. Whenever I was trying to negotiate with her regarding some difficulty we were having, she would say: "I don't want any of that 'social work talk," When the son of a minister friend of mine got all As in every school subject except religion, which he flunked, I started to catch on.

"If I don't stop taking responsibility for everyone, I'm going to burn up!"

Ralph is an ambitious, successful psychologist in his middle 30s. As part of his vacation plans he had elected to participate in a workshop on self-care for helping professionals. "It's hard to give up what I'm good at. I'm a good listener. In fact, people pay me a lot of money to listen to them. My heart feels open to people, and

I like that, but I take it in my gut. I feel so much responsibility, it can be overwhelming. Before I left town last Friday, I was running around like crazy trying to see everybody and get my clients all taken care of so I could have a week's vacation. Now I have to recover first before I have the energy to enjoy my time off."

Ralph describes his variation of burnout as "burning up." A moth is attracted to the flame but it doesn't have the intelligence to stop at a safe distance. Becoming self-caring means developing the ability to stop and pace ourselves so we do not continue cycles of overdoing followed by time out for healing and recovery. Self-care means noticing earlier and earlier how we are using ourselves so we can interrupt the patterns before we do irreversible damage to ourselves. The openness of Ralph's heart serves him well as a helping person, but he needs the skills to be empathic to his *own* needs and to listen to himself as well as to others. Rest sometimes needs to come before recreation, and these, like the other elements, need to be in balance with one another before self-care and self-healing can occur.

"The work gets so heavy, continually dealing with issues of life and death."

Ann is a registered nurse who had worked five years in the oncology ward with children who had cancer. "I found that work very rewarding, but I had to give it up a year ago. I'm working in the labor and delivery room now, where we have more good news than bad. I still have trouble with the bad things that happen to good people. Often, I can't get patients off my mind after the shift is over. In addition to that, we have to deal with the politics of the hospital. When I see what little budget support we get from the administration and all the infighting among groups, I just want to run away and join the circus."

One of the gifts we receive in witnessing birthing and dying is a clear understanding of what really matters. Recognizing what matters can establish, for us personally, a balance between the elements of *seriousness* and *humor*. Since many work organizations are not operating from a place of balanced perspective, maintaining our own balance can be more difficult. Like Ann, many of us see clearly what is wrong in our workplace and may have ideas to correct the situation. Recognizing that the work world is not the way we want it to be—and that it's not about to shape up to our liking any time soon—we can decide what to take seriously and act upon, and when to laugh and enjoy the ludicrous nature of the situation (*humor*). Regretfully there are situations that require leaving one's worksite or even one's occupation for the greater good of self-care and self-healing (*Letting Go*).

"When the client expresses emotion and cries, I lose touch."

Daniel is a massage therapist. He says, "I enjoy working with people, relieving their stresses and strains. I love to see the difference in people as they come in, tired and worn out, and as they leave, relaxed yet energized. However, when the client cries, I have trouble. I've always felt uncomfortable around someone crying. It probably goes back to the time after my dad left. My mother used to sit in her room and sob for hours. I felt so helpless. Now, when a client starts to cry, I find myself wanting to end the session as quickly as I possibly can."

Daniel is pointing out some of the key rewards and costs of being a professional helper. We often have the privilege of witnessing people's growth and transformations. And, as part of this process, we witness their fears and pain. *Pleasure* and *pain* are both essential elements for self-care and self-healing.

As Daniel describes it, when someone else's expression of emotions hooks into our own unresolved pain from the past, we're confronted with our own "demons." Intense work with people demands a willingness to face our own issues from the past (*Sorting and Separating*).

The choices are to see this as an opportunity to grow and learn, or to run for safety to another profession, one that doesn't involve such intense people contact. But not being one who earns a living as a helper doesn't mean that one is free from the strains of helping roles. Most of us spend a great deal of time caring for relatives. Meet Lisa.

"I'm just the cook, maid, chauffeur, and laundry woman."

Lisa is an attractive mother of three children, ages 10, 12, and 16. She is a full-time mom, a volunteer for her church, the wife of a professional man, and the only daughter to a father who is in poor health. "I've always wanted to be a mother, and I do think it is an important job. And I want to do right by my dad at this difficult time in his life. But there sure are times when I don't think anybody sees me except for what I can do for them. I give, give, give and they take, take, take. I want something for myself, something that doesn't involve being somebody's relative. And I long for some time to myself with no one wanting anything from me."

For most of us, our connections to others provide significant enrichment to our lives. But for our own self-care and self-healing, these *connections* must be balanced by *solitude*, by quiet time to listen and respond to our own inner needs. Healthy giving needs to be balanced by receiving. If not, our giving actions create resentment towards the very people who mean the most to us. In longing for a time when nobody will want anything from her, Lisa personifies the problem we codependent caregivers have in giving *ourselves* permission for our own self-care. As my friend Rose used to say, "We women are never out of relatives," nor will the relatives run out of wants and needs for us to fulfill.

Self-care and self-healing require that we demand time for ourselves (*solitude*), regardless of whether people need things from us or not. Training others to take over and relieve us from our family duties may be one of the most important steps in making self-care possible and in reducing our need for self-healing (*support* and *connection*).

"They just won't take responsibility for their own health!"

Gary, a participant in a self-care workshop, began describing his biggest problem as a dentist. "The hardest situation for me is when patients don't take their dental health seriously. They wait till they get a toothache in the middle of the night and then expect me to fix the damage. Even when I explain it to them, some will listen and some will continue to expect me to fix them up after the damage is done. Recently, I've made the connection between the backaches I get at the end of the day and the patients I see. When I see those frustrating patients, I go home with a backache. Other days, I can work long hours with no trouble. Another thing I know about myself that seems related here: I want my patients to like me, and I'm sure that is part of the problem."

In the healthcare field, practitioners talk about "patient compliance." People are considered "good" patients and clients when they do what the doctor says. We are making trouble for ourselves when we expect our students or patients (or adult children for that matter) to do what we say because we say it. The missing element here seems to be a balance between *support* and *challenge* in the partnership between helper and helpee. Gary supports his patients in taking care of their teeth and accepts the challenge of getting his message across. But having done his part, Gary needs to support himself and pass the challenge of caring and healing on to his patients, who are the only ones who have the power to meet it (*Letting Go and Surrendering*).

Self-care for helpers sometimes requires withdrawing our services, without malice, from people who have demonstrated an inability to benefit from our help.

"I feel I need some 'soul healing' myself."

Ted had been a psychiatrist for 20 years and would be 55 the next month. He explained, "The word 'psychiatry' comes from a Greek word that means 'soul healing,' and that's what I'd like to order for myself. Maybe the problem is my age, or too many years with too many people who are too sick to heal. Whatever it is, I feel stuck. Managing two offices and running back and forth between two hospitals feels like too much. A cell phone has made it easier to keep up with calls than it used to be, but now there's no quiet time. Even the patients seem all alike at this point, and I find myself wondering, is this why I went into medicine?"

It is possible to have too much of any good thing, and Ted's comments illustrate several elements of self-care out of balance in this way. He is sensing that his age has something to do with his discontent, and that seems quite likely since the proper balance between *movement* and *stillness*, or *variety* and *routine*, or *challenge* and *support* can be different at different times in our lives. What may have been exciting and challenging in Ted's 30s and 40s now may seem dull and routine.

Technology and specialization have created some new problems for caregivers while solving others. Like freeze-dried soups—they're efficient, but they're not as delicious or nutritious as the old-fashioned kind. The element of variety is missing when professionals and agencies specialize in serving one type of client or one problem condition. Burnout or compassion fatigue takes place faster when there isn't enough variety in the ways we use ourselves or in the types of challenges we are confronting. On the other hand, little comfort is received from routines that allow no time for human contact and support from coworkers and staff.

"I always went to workshops to learn things for my clients. This time I'm here for me."

Nancy is a psychiatric nurse who specializes in working with chemically dependent patients and their families. "I want to know how to stay emotionally in touch with the patients without becoming drained myself. Let's face it. Some of the people I work with are not pleasant to be around, especially in the early stages of their recovery. I find myself withdrawing behind my paperwork, but then even my staff feels shut out. I receive a lot from contact with some of the patients, but I guess I don't know how to keep clear boundaries without erecting a wall."

Bringing the focus back to herself is an important step in Nancy's self-caring. She is recognizing that the workshops are not only for what she can learn to help her patients, but also for her own benefit. Our needs count too, and, in the long run, taking care of ourselves means we are better able to carry out our caring work. Keeping clear boundaries between ourselves and others without erecting a wall involves finding a balance between *taking in* and *letting go*, knowing what we need for our own *nourishment* in relationships, and withdrawing when it is time for *abstinence*.

"Both my husband and I are workaholics."

"We've teased about it for years, but it's nothing to joke about," Maureen, a social worker in her late forties, told me. Maureen's voice was shaky, and tears rolled from the corners of her eyes as she made this admission to herself and to me. "The other morning I woke up angry at my husband, Jeff, who runs his own insurance agency. After we both had promised to stop overworking, he was leaving the house early for the third day in a row on top of having gotten home late the night before. We keep taking on more and more until we have no time together, no time for ourselves, and no energy left for enjoyment when we do get a day off."

Maureen continued, "Jeff and I did have a good talk over the phone after our angry words this morning. We both realized that we have the habit of just 'trying harder' when things start happening at work. Jeff gets anxious about money if he's not working overtime, and I start overdoing when I think people's needs aren't being met. We both seem to believe that if each of us does everything right, nothing will ever go wrong at work. Like other addictions, controlling our workaholism seems impossible. Jeff told me he kept saying the Serenity Prayer to himself after our argument: 'God, grant me the serenity to accept the things I cannot change, courage to change the things I can, and the wisdom to know the difference.'"[1]

The problem with having work as an addiction is that it *appears* so worthwhile. We are filling a need, accomplishing something, and earning money in the process. But eventually, when we've done too much of this good thing, we hurt ourselves and those around us. There's no time or energy for *play* or *rest* or *relaxation*. Maureen and Jeff have come a long way already in seeing their difficulties as a kind of addiction. Like people who realize that their drinking has gotten out of hand, they vow to control it. They make a plan, but gradually their resolve slips, and before long the drinking (or overworking) is back where it was before. In order to become self-caring, we caregivers, like Maureen and Jeff, must learn to set realistic boundaries on our working habits and stick to them. Like people who overdo with drugs or alcohol, those of us who overdo in our work can benefit from a twelve-step program to deal with our workaholism and our addiction to helping others.

"I need to find a way to have distance between myself and my 28-year-old son."

Annie was attending one of Christine's self-care retreats for the first time. She shared that her adult son had been in a major, life-threatening motorcycle accident. He lost both his legs and she has become his primary caregiver. They were both struggling through depression and unexpected grief and loss from the accident. "I feel like it's all my fault. After we'd had an argument he left the house and drove, even though he'd been drinking. Within days of coming home from the hospital he was abusing his meds, and I didn't tell the doctor. He recently had to go to the mental health hospital because he was hearing and seeing things that were not there and I couldn't help him."

By the end of the weekend Annie had begun to forgive herself. She developed self-care goals: to attend a local Al-Anon group regularly and to reach out to new social groups so her life could be about more than just caregiving and her home.

"I'm slowly losing my mom. Everyday she's not the same and I'm not the same."

Christine met Lynn at a women's self-care retreat she was offering near Atlanta. Lynn is a physical therapist by profession and an adult daughter who is caring for both of her parents, who live next door. Her mom is 88 and her dad is 90. "My sister is part of the caregiving team. The fact that we are in and out of our parents' home several times a day, helping with the shopping and cooking, means they are able to live 'independently' for now."

Since her mom is in early stage dementia, Lynn recognized that she needed more support and decided to attend the self-care weekend, and she invited her grown daughter (caregiver to a family of five) to join her. More than 44 million people in the United States are informal caretakers for loved ones in their home. Currently, 72 percent of caregivers take care of someone 50 or older.[2] Self-care for the caregivers is essential to maintaining this routine. Lynn sought out and attended the retreat because she needed a break. When caring for others it is easy to lose oneself in the daily grind that tending to multiple people entails, and it is essential to do things to avoid losing yourself this way. Take time out and do one thing a day for yourself—take a walk outside, read a book, or even take a nap; at the retreat Lynn was able to do all these things. Healthy, delicious meals were provided, and there was time for walks, meditation, long conversations with her adult daughter, and sleep. She left recharged and renewed.

Your Continuum of Self-Care Elements

How balanced are some of the key self-care elements in your life? A balanced life, like a balanced diet, means that we don't have too much of any one thing while experiencing a deficiency of other necessary elements. Self-care and self-healing result when we discover what we need, and find ways to integrate those needs into our lives, keeping in mind our need for balance.

People who have a problem maintaining optimum weight often use food to satisfy other (non-nutritional) needs. Food can be used for comfort, to energize, or to reward oneself. Food can also be a way to avoid experiencing and dealing with unpleasant feelings. Stuffing ourselves with food can be a way of stuffing our feelings as well.

We can overdo other things besides food. Often we have too much of a good thing, as we tend to rely on one activity, substance, or relationship to fill all our needs. Maybe it's jogging or aerobics or gambling or sex or alcohol or other drugs. We can overdo using work or helping others in our personal life to give us a sense of worth, security, and identity. The list of potentially addictive things is endless, but the damaging result to our self-care and self-healing is the same for all of them.

We can interrupt this pattern of using something as our one and only "fix" by identifying what element is missing. Rather than thinking of a "fix," like an on-off light switch, imagine a continuum (like a rheostat or dimmer on a light switch) between related self-care elements. Rather than thinking of good elements, which we continually want to increase in our lives, and bad elements, which we work to avoid—think of all of life's elements as necessary, each with its own benefit, each with its own part in our balance. When we don't feel our own pain, we cannot discern when something is wrong. When we feel only pain, we miss out on life's pleasures. Time alone can be important to our self-care, but too much turns into isolation. Experiencing connection to others is one of the things that life is about, but when we don't have time to ourselves, we have less and less to give to others. Use the following self-test to see where you are at this point in time in relation to some key self-care elements.

SELF-CARE ELEMENTS: A SELF-TEST

On each of the following lines, place an **X** to represent where you are today in regard to each of the pairs of elements listed. If the two elements on the same line feel in balance right now, your **X** will be near the center. If one of the elements is overrepresented in your life at the present time, your **X** will be closer to that element and farther away from the one that is underrepresented.

movement..stillness

work...play

nourishment..abstinence

seriousness..humor

pleasure...pain

challenge ....support

solitude...connection

variety...routine

recreation...rest

taking in..letting go

Notice the elements that seem most absent from your life. In the space below identify ways to include them, avoiding ways that are immoral, illegal, or fattening.

_____

_____

_____

Go back and circle the element(s) that you want to focus on, especially for the coming week. Remember, balance and harmony are your goals, so take care not to take on too many elements at one time. Next week you can take the self-test again and see what a difference the missing element(s) has made in the balance of your continuum of self-care. Since this is not an exhaustive list, you may want to add your own elements as you become more familiar with this way of thinking.

Remember, each time you complete the test you have created a snapshot of one point in time. To get a moving picture of your patterns over time, you will need to repeat the test on a regular basis for a while and compare your results.

BE AWARE OF REMEDIES

We started this chapter with the caution that there is danger in the telling of the tale. Let's finish by remembering there is danger in *remedies* as well as in the ways they are administered. The above instrument and any of the other tools and techniques suggested in this book are just that. Use them as suggestions. Allow them to stimulate your thinking in a different direction or to interrupt your usual pattern of behaving. Use them gently, with kindness to yourself. If you find something here that doesn't move you in the direction of self-care and self-healing, or if and when it outlives its usefulness, discard it, and create your own. You are the only *real* expert on you and your own experience, and your own body wisdom is your most reliable guide.

Act Two

Stage and Settings

The caregiver's dance of self-care/self-healing cannot be a solo, limited to private spaces and times we are alone. Caregivers perform a communal dance, in step with others in the workplace and at home. Attending to the setting where caregiving happens helps us identify whether we have the necessary props to perform our roles. We ask, does the place where we do our work support us as well as support what we are trying to accomplish there? For caregivers whose workplace is also their home—is there a place for privacy, a place where you can be offstage? And what of the supporting cast? The intricate dance of balancing our own needs with the needs of others may receive little applause unless we carefully select partners, friends, and colleagues who know how to take care of themselves.

In the next three chapters we look at the subtle (and not so subtle) aspects of the stage and setting where we perform the movements of our daily lives. We look at actions to take and situations to avoid, so we may move gracefully and harmoniously in our offices and homes and (for some of us) in our relationships to large organizations.

*Dance is the only art wherein
we ourselves are the stuff
of which it is made.*

–Ted Shawn

3

A Self-Caring Workplace

Mary, Mary, quite contrary, how does your garden grow?
With silver bells and cockle shells,
and pretty maids all in a row.
–Mother Goose nursery rhyme

The question that no one has bothered to ask here is, why is Mary so contrary? Is she not happy with the silver bells of her cell phone, computer, and social media platform? How about the text messages she answers and the FaceBook stream she responds to? Perhaps rocks and weeds are crowding out her seedlings and neighborhood roughnecks have been digging up her bulbs and trampling her blooms. Unlike the nursery rhyme, it must be here stated that having cell phones to ring and email and Instagram messages to keep track of does not a working, peaceful garden make. We are on the right track if we think of spaces and places where we work as gardens. People, like plants, can bloom where they are planted only if conditions exist to support growth. In this chapter we will be looking at the important conditions necessary to do the dance of self-care and self-healing in the workplace. And if you are like more and more people today whose workplace is your home place, we'll look for ways to be self-caring in that challenging situation.

First we explore the match between the person you are and the type of work you are doing. Next we look at the physical environment and how the workspace itself contributes to or detracts from the type of work you are attempting to accomplish there. We look at low-budget efforts you can make to help your workplace become more compatible with your needs. Finally, we discuss some actions to enable you to work in a self-caring way in whatever environment your caregiving tasks take you into.

The Critical Match

The fact that we are able to do certain work doesn't mean it is the right work for us. The importance of the match between a person and the type of work he or she does was taught to me by a client I will call Matthew.

MATTHEW'S DISCONTENT

When Matthew was 35 years old he came to me expressing extreme dissatisfaction with his work life. He performed his job well, giving each task caring attention. His supervisors and employers were pleased with his performance. His family told him that he'd better hold on to his good job since good jobs were hard to find. But still, he felt unfulfilled and unhappy.

While he was in a state of deep relaxation, I asked Matthew to go back and remember what ideas he had about work when he was a little boy. He remembered playing with trucks and blocks and erector sets and, in the voice of his younger self, he said, "Work means to build things that last."

And why was Matthew's present job such a mismatch with who he really was? Each day he stocked merchandise on shelves from which people on the next shift filled orders. Each day when he returned to work, his finely organized patterns, the symmetrical rows he had carefully constructed, were all destroyed. No mystery his discontent, this assault on his soul each day of his work life.

Hopefully, you have a better match between your values about work and the actual work that you do. If you don't, and the mismatch is anywhere near as troubling as Matthew's, the most self-caring, self-healing act you can perform is a career change. Being a professional caregiver can be rewarding and fulfilling, but not if you have always wanted to be a forest ranger or a deep-sea diver.

AUTHOR REFLECTIONS

Christine: I worked at a nonprofit social service agency that I loved for close to 10 years. I started out as a case manager, became a recruiter and trainer, and eventually accepted a position as the development director. The pay was substantially better. I enjoyed the work, but the downside was that it created a lot of stress and "dis-ease" in my body. As I reflect back on this time in my life, I realize that one of the things creating stress for me was the fact that I was off my path. I was no longer seeing and serving individual clients. One of the reasons I picked social work for my bachelor's and master's degrees, besides the fact that it was my passion, was that the degree provided many avenues and areas for work in case of burnout with one particular type of client or situation.

I loved the agency I worked for and the people I worked with, but when I had a major health scare due to stress, overwork, and not taking care of myself, I had to make a change. I decided to resign from the full-time development director job and work as a contract social worker, primarily doing training and consulting. I had control of my hours and what jobs I took on. ❋

Sheila: My coming into the field of social work from performing and teaching dance was a transition few people understood at the time. But something in me saw the connection. My university class on group dynamics met on Thursday afternoons, just after I taught creative dance to three- and five-year-olds in the morning, and before I taught dance to a group of women at a nearby community college in the afternoon. To accommodate my young children's babysitter and my budget, it all had to take place on the same day.

Years later, after I had shared movement and theater games with my social work students and brought dance and music into my therapy groups, I began describing myself as "a dancing social worker." This "both, and" identity made taking care of myself more difficult on some occasions, as I felt a misunderstood outsider in both environments. The upside has been that I have had the opportunity to exercise more variations of my own creativity, resulting in a more satisfying life than I would have had otherwise. ✿

If we continue with the analogy of the workplace as a garden and people as the plants that try to bloom there, consider yourself, through the magic of your own imagination, in a waltz of the flowers.

WALTZ OF THE FLOWERS: A FLOWER FANTASY

What if you were a valuable, delicate plant in need of a specific type of environment that would enable you to survive and thrive? Do you know what type of plant you are and what conditions are necessary for your own blooming? Read through the following exercise, and then give yourself the gift of a few minutes to explore the activity on your own.

Consider the incredible variety of types of flowering plants! There are tall and short shrubs, and shy and bold flowers. You will find brilliantly colored blooms growing in likely and unlikely places, singly and in clusters, on broad meadows and narrow ledges.

When you walk through a garden, notice not only the variety of flowers but the variety of their preferred surroundings as well. There are sunny and shady spots and a variety of soils, dry and sandy, or moist and mossy. While some types of flowers thrive best in rock gardens, others need marshlands or a small pond for their best nourishment. While some plants need frequent watering, others, like the cactus, store their own water from one season to the next.

Some flowers bloom all summer, others in fall, and others bloom only once every few years. And plants have many ways of relating to the environment as well. Some vines need latticework to climb. Others, like Texas bluebonnets, send chemicals into the soil to change the surrounding area. This causes other plants to die back, and gives the bluebonnets the needed room to grow.

Even amateur gardeners can tell you that whatever knowledge you have of soils and fertilizers, of sprinkling systems and weather conditions, the major mystery in creating a successful garden is the locating of particular plants in the place where their needs are met.

So imagine yourself as a flower.

- Do you notice a sturdy stalk or stem, or do you see yourself climbing a wall or an arching cornice?
- Do you thrive in the summer heat, or do you fare better in sheltering shade?
- Are you able to bloom in a window box overlooking a city street? Perhaps you would feel more at home in a terra-cotta container on the back patio.
- Do you do better surrounded by other flowers, or are you a loner bud who likes lots of elbow room?
- How about being planted in rows and neat, straight-lined beds—or would a random pattern suit your temperament best?
- What type of head gardener or nursery person would you like? Someone who plots and plans down to the smallest detail, or one who tills and sows, provides plenty of fertilizer, and then lets nature take its course?

Allow images of flowers and gardens, pictures of parks and nature settings to appear in the window of your inner mind. Appreciate and enjoy the images of the various types of flowers until you notice that one particular image keeps returning to you. After you have discovered your attraction to this special species of flower, imagine yourself as that flower. Describe yourself as that flower:

"I am a _____ (name flower).
My petals are _____ .
I grow best in _____ and with_____ .
I need lots of _____ and I especially enjoy
_____ ."

Take note of what you have discovered about yourself in this flower fantasy. This image of yourself as a flower comes from the right side of your brain and may contain information that is not available when you are using only the left, analytical side.

Share what you experienced in this fantasy with someone who knows you well. It might also be fun to look up the official description of the flower you visualized in your fantasy. What does it require to grow and bloom, remembering that we, as part of nature, cannot bloom all the time? There must be times of dormancy and rest.

Your Own Workplace

When you feel certain about the kind of flower (worker) you are and you have a match between yourself and the type of work you are doing, it's time to think about the place where you do most of your work. What does this place feel like, this place where you spend so much of your time? Is it nourishing or draining of your energies? Do you ever see the light of day, the natural light so necessary for plants and other living things? How far do you have to go for a breath of fresh air? What is the view from your workstation? Restful? Boring? Invigorating?

What about sound? Noise pollution can be draining as you work to screen out distracting sounds. On the other hand, the sound of falling water or some "white noise" machines can invoke a restful, meditative state that aids concentration.

Listen as a group of caregivers discuss their workplaces with me, the places where caring, helping, and healing are supposed to happen. After the group had taken a few minutes to image themselves as flowers and then to picture their current work environments, Judith began the discussion:

"I pictured myself as a water lily in a quiet, cool, shady pond. When I think about my work environment, I see the color orange. That's the color they have painted the staff areas of the hospital where I work. The activity in these areas is hurried and hectic and, of course, very crowded. In the areas where the patients are, care has been taken to have relaxing colors, but in the trenches . . . !"

"It's the same thing at the facilities where I consult," Chris remarked. "Sometimes I ask myself, if I'm supposed to have so much authority, how come I don't have a place to sit down?"

Helen added her discoveries from the exercise: "I realized just how bad some of my working conditions are. In the adult day care centers where I work, the buildings are old, and the heating and cooling is difficult to regulate. In the summer, the temperature is often over 90 degrees, and I am trying to do activities with 21 people in not nearly enough space."

"The temperature in newer business buildings isn't that easy to regulate, either," I said. "I was presenting a seminar for bank employees in the late afternoon, after the bank had closed to the public. As I was speaking to the staff in the main lobby, the area was becoming hotter and more uncomfortable by the minute. When I inquired, I was told that the air conditioning was on a timer controlled from downtown. So, when the customers leave, the Texas heat is allowed to enter."

"Sends quite a message of management's regard for their employees," Mark, a rehab counselor, said.

"I was thinking of the air in the building where I work," Susan remarked. "It's better now that they don't let people smoke at their desks, but the air still gets stuffy and stale. And of course, when they remodeled our building they fixed the windows so you can't open them."

"When you mentioned not having a place to sit down to review records, I thought about the nightmarish furniture in the places where teaching and learning are supposed to be taking place," Dennis, a high school teacher, said. "It seems like I'm forever moving furniture unless, of course, I get one of those classrooms where the chairs are bolted to the floor!"

"When I imagine my ideal work environment, I see plants and sunlight, and hear natural sounds of water and birds," Shirley said, "in contrast to the real world, where I have on several occasions had offices without windows."

"In one counseling center where I worked in an office without windows, I took some pretty drastic action," I told the group. "I turned my desk to the corner and, to put in the open triangle between the walls and my desk, I brought in a bunch of plants. I rigged grow lights from the ceiling to keep the plants alive, and, as the plants flourished, it did wonders for my spirit."

The Power of the Physical Environment

Visiting with Ralph Caplan, a designer and writer who consults on workspaces, I came to appreciate the power of the environment to affect our comfort level, our ability to focus and concentrate, and, finally, our sense of ourselves. Caplan has said it well in some poems he wrote for an ad campaign to promote office systems.

Everybody needs a Here.
A nest, a niche,
a room of one's own.
A space with enough
of its own character
to accept yours.
A corner that belongs to you
as much as you belong to it.

Somewhere you know
that knows you:
a homeroom at school,
a familiar street, a ship in port.

Anywhere that welcomes
you back when
there is no one there to say it.
A sense of place, solid enough
for light to break against.

No one wants to be nowhere.
Or closed in.
Any environment is wrong
if you feel stuck in it.
A sense of place,
a sense of light
and openness,
a sense of choice.
These are qualities we seek
in the spaces where we live.
And work.[1]

Ralph reminded me that "in the workplace the environment encourages certain types of behaviors, such as collaboration or discussion or solitary concentration. Or the environment discourages such activities."[2] And if your caregiving work is done at, or from, your home?

AUTHOR REFLECTIONS

Sheila: My kitchen counter is my favorite place to do computer work. It's just the right height to be my standing desk. It's full of light from the kitchen windows and, since I live on a river, I even have a view of the slow-moving barges. But when I'm skyping with a client, I need more privacy. I still haven't solved the problem of convenient space for my files, and I still tend to stay too long at creative writing tasks. I've imagined a timer that would speak in the commanding voice of a god or goddess: "Kindly step away from the screen."

Christine: I have two places that I work from at home. My first office has a desk, bookshelves, a view of the tall trees in my backyard, and importantly, a door that shuts. This is where I do my video conference calls with clients and where I go when I need uninterrupted work time for writing. I enjoy lighting a candle and setting the tone for what I'm working on.

When I am checking tasks off my list, working in short bursts, I like to work from my kitchen table. I'm on my laptop and in the center of things. For my self-care, I know that I need to change locations often, to get up, stretch my body, and move. Different times during the day call for different locations. Some of my colleagues like to work at coffee shops, but I get too distracted for that to be a good, productive, and self-caring place for me to work.

A Self-Caring Workplace

"With all the studies on color and its effect on mood, the most important factor may be whether people can pick the color, whether people have even the illusion of choice," Ralph continued in our discussion on creating healthy work environments.

"I guess, since the environment has such a strong impact on us, even dictating our behavior at times, to be self-caring we need to consider the environment and make what choices we can about it," I said.

"Yes, probably one of the worst things that can happen in life is to feel stuck, and in the workplace people often don't exercise the potential choices that are there. According to our research, the trouble with adjustable chairs is that people often fail to adjust them," Mr. Caplan concluded.

Taking care of one's self in the workplace sometimes means acting on your own behalf to change or alter your working environment. Like the plants that send chemicals into the soil to create a better place for their own growing, you may need to alter aspects of your physical work environment. *Exercising Choice* is a self-care skill as well as a significant part of work satisfaction.

Look at the physical environment around you and discover what changes need to be made so that your workspace fits you and the work you do in it. As an example, let's start with something basic. What about the chair you are sitting in and the work surface it connects with?

What's in a Chair?

Most people are conscious of the need for a good night's sleep and of the important role a good mattress plays in meeting this need. But we are often less focused on the chairs we sit in while we work. Lower back pain is the most frequent cause of absenteeism in the workplace, and the chairs we sit in are major contributors to this ailment. Yet people often object to spending a bit more money for chairs that have been designed with the human frame in mind.

Sitting in most chairs means that we give up our own self-support. By sitting in chairs with the so-called "bucket" design, we collapse into cushions that feel comfortable initially. But, as with the too-soft mattress, we don't get enough support and we are exhausted at the end of the day. After months and years of living like this, we lose the ability to support ourselves in a sitting position. What is needed in a chair is a supportive structure that encourages supporting oneself.

Chairs, like people, come in all sorts of shapes and sizes. Unfortunately, the shapes and sizes of chairs do not always correspond to the shapes and sizes of people. As with shoes, there is no substitute for trying the chairs on, moving around in them, and pulling them up to a workstation. Remember too, no chair is good for your body for very long, so plan to take breaks and change positions often. Recent research has determined that sitting is the new smoking as far as life expectancy is concerned. Sitting for prolonged periods of time has been linked to heart disease, depression, diabetes, and a higher risk of being disabled.[3]

Here are some suggestions to reduce the time you're sitting during the day:

- Stand while talking on the phone.
- Set your computer on a standing desk or counter top.
- In good weather hold a meeting with colleagues while walking in nature.
- Set a timer to call you to a 10-minute standing, stretching, moving, or other interruption.

More About Your Physical Environment
What About Lighting?

When I interviewed designers of workspaces, they named light as the first and most important consideration for healthy worksites. I asked the question, "If you didn't have much money to spend, what suggestions would you make to improve a work environment?" The answer came back, "Focus on your lighting! Replace fluorescent lights with full-spectrum bulbs (lights that contain all the colors of natural sunlight) and use task lighting." (Task lighting spotlights the area where light is needed for particular tasks.)[4]

Many of us remember, when we were children, having teachers and parents remind us of the importance of having enough light on our books and papers. Insufficient lighting creates eye strain, which causes headaches, which take a lot of the fun and pleasure from our work day. Flexibility in light sources is important when we are looking at a computer screen. A small change in the angle of light hitting the screen or paper in front of us can conserve the energy we may be wasting, as we are staring and straining to see.

A More Comfortable Workplace

Speaking of seeing, what is your view from your workstation? We want protection from distractions, but a lack of visual stimulation in the environment is not the answer. And what about sound? Let's ask some other caregivers to discuss what they have done to give their workspaces a sense of place, to create a feeling for themselves of being "at home" where they work:

Sharon, a manager for a retail company, began by telling the group of her experiences in the corporate world. "Some companies and work organizations won't allow employees to decorate their offices with personal items because it takes away from the corporate image they are trying to portray. I can appreciate the need for some consistency in the overall design of the building, but it's important for me that my office reflects something of who I am and what I do there. I always bring a few items from home to give me a sense of continuity and the comfort of familiar surroundings."

"I like being able to surround myself with pictures that have some personal meaning to me," Susan, a drug abuse counselor, commented. "I like pictures of my family, along with some pictures that remind me of places where I have felt especially good, like the mountains or the seashore."

"I have a sandbox in my office," the psychologist Ralph boasted. "Well, 'box' is a bit of an exaggeration. It's actually an old ashtray that, when we went to a smoke-free workplace, I filled with sand and miniature stones and shells from my trips to the beach. Not only does it remind me of a favorite spot, but I can recapture some of that mellow 'beach feeling' playing with the sand between my fingers while I'm returning phone calls."

"Music is an important way for me to stay in a mellow place," a nurse, Ruth Ann, admitted. "I always found it helpful to play tapes of relaxing music in my car on the way in to the office in the morning. Finally, it dawned on me that this kind of music would be helpful to the patients and staff in the doctor's office where I work. I don't mean that elevator kind of music, but music that seems to go with the sounds and rhythms of nature."

Anne, another nurse, joined in. "We have been using music in the labor and delivery rooms for quite a while now, and I think it has made quite a difference. Even when the situations get tense and a bit frantic, at least there's a rhythm to it all." Studies show that the planned use of music by mothers and caregivers can be an aid to prenatal preparation and an important adjunct in pain and stress management during labor and birth.[5]

Working in a Self-Caring Way

How can we tell if we've been working in a self-caring way? Notice how much energy you have left for your own life at the end of the workday. Do you stumble home and immediately collapse into a sofa or bed? Are you too tired to eat? Or do you eat everything in sight, feeling the need for an energy transfusion? If staring at the TV or computer screen is the extent of your off-duty recreation, you may need to give yourself more frequent breaks during your day.

There is an African dialect in which the word for "work" is the same as the word for "dance." Once I learned that, I started asking myself at the end of the day, "How did the dance go today?" Viewing work as a dance, we would consider altering our rhythm and patterns. If work were a dance, we'd experience a variety of movements, faster segments followed by slower ones, and frequent pauses to rest. We'd be "going the speed of our bodies," as we say in InterPlay, pacing ourselves, and focusing our energy on the specific steps at hand. There would be no such thing as "hurry up," and rather than continually asking "What's next?" we would pause to experience the joy of celebrating our accomplishments along the way.

SUPPORTIVE WORK FRIENDS

The family therapist Carl Whitaker recommends that everybody find what he calls a "cuddle group." This is a group of friends who accept you unconditionally and who meet solely for the purpose of supporting and celebrating each member. The more demanding and stress-provoking the job, the more necessary the "cuddle group."

The group can be as small as two people, as large as ten or twelve. It can be at the worksite or nearby. A woman colleague and I pledged to meet for dinner one evening a week when we both work late. Our commitment to each other helps us resist the urge to make one more phone call or linger to catch up on paperwork. Instead, we take care of ourselves with nourishing food and conversation.

My husband has several men friends who refer to themselves as "cave buds." They checked in with each other by phone during hectic workdays for years. And still, 25 years later, they continue to support one another by arranging golf getaway vacations once a year.

Another friend and I realized that, due to my leaving the university where I worked, we would no longer see one another at work. To insure continued contact, we agreed to meet monthly for an extended lunch. We considered inviting other caregivers to join what we called our "Sappy Social Workers' Support Group," but somehow we never got around to it. We discussed our health, current work challenges, family crises, whatever came up in our lives. Fourteen years later, when Colleen lay dying from ovarian cancer, she told me, "I never thought we would become so deeply connected and such long-term friends." Like the Little Prince's regular visit to his special friend, what a gift those monthly luncheons turned out to be.

Creating a Supportive Team

Several years ago, as the world seemed to be tumbling down around my head career-wise, I got the opportunity to re-create my work life. A nurse/manager friend and her husband, a financial planner, led my husband and me in a career/life planning workshop. With flip chart and magic markers in hand, they encouraged us to dream and create our best-case scenario. We developed a plan, and in only eight months, the actuality of a holistic mental health clinic and group practice was realized. We experienced for the first time the joys and struggles of designing with graph paper, making a business plan, and dealing with bankers, architects, accountants, and construction contractors. None of these were as difficult and time consuming as learning to build a collaborative work team. After much trial and error, we got far enough along in our own self-healing to let go of what wasn't working in order to encourage and welcome people and things that did work.

We learned to say what we wanted while trying not to talk anyone into anything. We learned to consult with others, both staff and outside experts, and then to make the necessary decisions that were ours alone to make. We learned to face the reality that we couldn't keep everybody happy all the time and take care of ourselves in the process. We knew from the beginning the importance of recognizing and rewarding achievement and celebrating personal and group accomplishments. It took practice, learning to develop the following attitudes:

● *Mistakes are natural events on the way to getting it right.* I knew an organization that gave an award for the most creative mistake of the month. Creative mistakes are celebrated because they demonstrate that the person is learning something new or discovering the need for improvements in the system. Too-frequent mistakes on the job can signal the need for diversion or rest from the work task. Or frequent mistakes may also mean an employee's personal stress is spilling over onto the workplace.

● *Workers have personal lives and sometimes need time off from work to take care of family business.* We alternated emergency week-end coverage among professional staff so people could have holidays and weekends off while still seeing that the needs of clients were met. Offering access to counseling for support staff members going through family crises, or arranging a temporary job reassignment, has paid off in increased work efficiency.

● *Work groups need practice in order to develop proficiency as a team.* The fact that people know their own job doesn't mean they understand what the organization is trying to accomplish, what other staff members do, or how their work roles fit together. Periodic staff retreats provide support staff, professionals, and consultants with the opportunity to get together in a relaxed environment to discover ways to work together and to refine their skills of collaboration.

● *A commitment to telling the truth is necessary for a supportive team to develop and grow through time.* As in our personal lives, in work teams we need to be able to work out differences and disagreements without blaming or shaming ourselves or others. We need to be able to show our vulnerabilities and allow others to show theirs as well. Continuing to pretend that everything is fine when it isn't, or that we don't care when we do, leads to a situation in which we no longer care to stay in that workplace. A staff member found the following item and posted it in the break room because she felt it was reflective of what we were trying to accomplish at our workplace.

CELEBRATION POLICY

We publically recognize achievements.
We encourage spontaneous celebrations.
We know that, if we're having fun, we work harder,
smarter, and longer.
We evaluate managers on their ability to create an
environment in which it is a pleasure to work.
Employees who spread gloom will be asked to leave.[6]

SIGNS FOR YOUR OFFICE WALL

Since working in a self-caring way involves what we tell ourselves and what we present to others, we can all use continual reminders of ways to take care of ourselves. As you decorate your workspace, consider the following signs for your desk or workspace walls. Invent your own friendly reminders for working in a self-care way.

Celebrate Each Accomplishment
In its moment, then celebrate yourself in each moment.

Note to self: Work is not the way I earn my worth.

SIGN FOR OTHERS:

Your failure to meet your deadlines does not
constitute an emergency for me.

(YOUR OWN SPECIAL SIGN):

After I came to understand what my husband called my AID (Attention *Intensity* Disorder), I wrote the following prayer. It reminds me that overdoing work can be too much of a good thing, damaging to health and well-being, and a definite detriment to self-care. When we get caught in this overdoing of work, we need to become self-healing. Like people who overdo drinking or eating, we need help from our Higher Power, or the God or Goddess of our understanding. Try repeating the following prayer on a daily basis, or write a prayer in your own words.

Prayer of a Recovering Workaholic

May I do today the work
which is truly mine to do
and support others in doing their duty as well.
May I take short breaks to catch my breath
and vary my tasks to prevent wearing myself out.
May I work with others in a partnership way,
celebrating all of our energies and talents.
May I communicate clearly my wants and needs
and listen to others from a receptive place of calm.
May I trust that my efforts,
however limited,
will bring—eventually—
a positive outcome.
Allow me to feel finished at the end of each day.
May my relationship with time be a flowing duet.
Meanwhile,
help me to let go of my illusions of
grandiose accomplishments,
of expecting of myself impossible feats.
And, most especially,
help me stop fighting the inevitable.

Doing Your Work as a Dance

Now let's review and apply Psyche's skills of self-care to your work situation. This is an excellent way to ensure that your work is a dance celebrating your values, gifts, and abilities. The first step combines two of Psyche's skills, *Stepping Back* and *Sorting and Separating*.

a) *Step Back* to gain a broader perspective and dream about your best-case work scenario. Next look at your current work environment and what is actually provided there. As you *Sort and Separate* your needs and values from what is actually provided in your work environment, you will gain information with which to *Exercise Choice*.

b) Call on the help of supportive friends from inside and outside your workplace. (*Partnership Power*)

c) If you determine that there are aspects of the work culture that interfere with your self-care, work on *Letting Go* of whatever it is you do to cooperate with these forces. In the interest of your self-care, you may need to *Let Go* of potential promotions, specific financial rewards, or the prestige that comes from over-working, losing sleep, and encouraging others to do likewise.

d) *Exercise Choice* in the way you treat yourself. Make changes in aspects of your work environment that you have some say over. Alter your rhythm and patterns of working, allowing for variety, rest, and recovery. And don't forget to celebrate your efforts and accomplishments and find colleagues to assist you.

Note: Sarah Brown has an incredible personalized tool for self-assessment in work and relationships. Christine uses it for her coaching clients and knows it makes the coaching relationship more efficient and effective. Check out the Book of You at www.bookofyou.com.

*If I can't dance I don't want
to be part of your revolution.*
–Emma Goldman

4

Self-Care in a Large Organization

*In legend there is relief from the enemy, sorrow is
turned into gladness, mourning into holiday.
In life, only some of this is possible.*

–E. M. Broner, *A Weave of Women*

In addition to the physical aspects of one's environment (space, furniture, color, sound, and light), many workplaces are also complex
social and organizational structures. Not simply an enactment of the
job descriptions and organizational flow charts, the workplace culture
dictates behaviors, moods, and relationships. Many of the factors that
affect the culture of the workplace are hidden from view. Even though
you have tended to the physical work environment, established friends
both inside and outside your workplace, and practiced doing your work
as a dance, your self-care is still not insured.

Working in a Dysfunctional Organization

Since people who haven't done their own inner work often act to recre-
ate the dysfunctional patterns familiar to them from their own families,
there are probably as many dysfunctional organizations (corporations,

governmental organizations, small businesses) as there are dysfunctional families. And employees, like the children in a dysfunctional family, often feel the negative effects of problems at the executive level without knowing the story behind the scenes. Meet my friend, Julie.

JULIE AND THE SINKING SHIP

It was early Saturday morning when I got the call. Julie had just begun to figure out what had been happening to her at the treatment center where she works. "I had been feeling emotionally abused for some time, but after yesterday it seems more like emotional rape, a betrayal by my supervisor," Julie told me.

As we began to talk about her situation, Julie expressed a feeling of guilt for intruding on my personal time, especially since I hadn't heard from her in months. "I've been working 60 to 70 hours a week, so I haven't had time for anything else lately," she said.

"I'm writing this morning on self-care in the workplace, and it sounds like your experiences are pretty relevant to my topic, so fire away!" I told her. "How did you happen to work such long hours?"

"I'm sure it's from a need to get the job done. The turnover in staff has been incredible. I've been a therapist on the unit for a little over six months, and I've been there the longest. My original plan was to complete my thesis while I continued working. It finally became clear to me how impossible that plan was. I spoke to my supervisor last week asking for a leave of absence. He seemed supportive of the idea at the time, but after the way he attacked me at the meeting yesterday in front of the whole team—I don't know where he stands."

After getting more details of the events of the last few months, the infighting among staff members, the discrepancy between what is said in private conversations and what happens in public meetings, and most of all, the splitting among staff members into "good parent / bad parent" roles in relation to the patients, I concluded, "You have a sick system and, just like a dysfunctional family, it's contagious, affecting everyone in it."

"That's what I've been feeling, but what the staff says is that we are getting more seriously disturbed patients lately," Julie said.

"It's interactive," I said. "With the kind of staff turnover you've had, you're not providing a stable environment, and patients pick up and magnify the instability in the environment. One of my colleagues did biofeedback with patients in a treatment center for a number of years. She noted that she could always tell when an administrative change was in the process of occurring because the baseline readings of all the patients in biofeedback therapy became higher than usual. And the readings for staff were even more elevated. This is hazardous work that we do, Julie, and staff can pick up the diseases of patients and administrators and add them to our own."

"This is what I am being accused of," Julie said. "There is one patient who is being scapegoated because he reacts to the environment. Whenever I take up for him, I become the scapegoat."

As we continued our telephone conversation, I glanced down at the manuscript in front of me, a page about the skills of self-care, and realized that Julie and I were moving through each of them. Julie began *Building and Using Partnership Power* when she reached out to me, overcoming her reticence to disturb my personal time. Together we began *Sorting and Separating* what part of her situation belongs to her and what belongs to others. Since I was an outsider to her specific situation but an insider to the kind of work she does and the type of facility where she works, we could *Step Back* together and see the big picture and the relationship of parts.

After Julie told me of her feelings of responsibility to her patients and their families, her concerns about her relationship to her supervisors, and her need to finish her degree, I told her, "I can put my advice to you into two words, Julie. Save yourself!"

As we talked about her *Letting Go and Surrendering* in the face of overwhelming odds she said, "I'm beginning to feel a weight lifting from my shoulders."

"You really don't have the power to change this situation. You are not the captain, and you don't have to go down with the ship. Use your power to save yourself, for yourself and for all the people you will be able to help once you complete your degree." I reminded her of her gifts and strengths and of the potential opportunities she could have when *Exercising Choice*.

"Now I feel my heart opening, and I'm getting images of other possibilities as we speak," As the conversation ended she said, "It really is all right to save myself, isn't it!"

Looking at Your Own Work Organization

As Julie's experience has so clearly illustrated, some work environments make self-care and self-healing next to impossible, and attempting to take any action to change things may entail grave risk. But not taking action will have ramifications, too. Remembering our waltz of the flowers, staying in a situation that is unhealthy for plants and other living things could carry the greatest risk of all. Before you consider taking any action in your workplace, take the following antidote to martyrdom. Repeat the following affirmation several times a day for at least three days before proceeding.

I matter. I am as precious and valuable as any one or all of my projects, goals, and achievements. I matter as much as all my past, present, and future accomplishments.

Working in a War Zone

In order to be able to take care of yourself at your work, you must first make sure that you are not working in a war zone. And self-care requires that if you are considering a job change, you make sure that the new work environment is a garden where you can blossom, not a war zone where you will be continually at risk. The following two checklists are offered for your consideration as you determine whether you are working in a war zone or about to sign up to work in one, and how to survive when you're in one.

How to Know if You Are Working in a War Zone

At first glance it would seem simple to determine if the organization where you work is operating as a war zone. In the case of open hostility, announced reorganizations, published threats of reprisal, and formal, confirmed notice of takeover attempt (both internal and external), a state of war is quite clear. However, by that time one or all of the following have probably already occurred:

- You have been fired, or your boss has been fired, which amounts to the same thing, though in that case your demise may be slower.
- Your best friend and colleague has been fired, so that all the fun and enjoyment has gone as you serve what could be a life sentence until retirement.
- You have quit and landed on your feet at a place that doesn't seem any better than the last one, but they pay you more hush money.

One of the major steps in becoming resilient is early identification of environmental stressors. "These boots were made for walking" is a refrain to sing while there is still breath left for singing and some spring left in one's gait. Becoming expert in self-care means not going to the place of undue stress in the first place, like the martial arts master who, sensing the energy of an approaching enemy, crosses the street and is not there when the enemy arrives.

To accomplish this slight-of-foot dance routine usually demands advanced skills of assessment, premonition, and more than a little inside information. It is in this spirit that the following advice is offered. (If you already know that your workplace is a war zone, see the next checklist below, "How To Be Self-Caring While Working In A War Zone." If you are unclear about whether the work setting you are currently in, or are considering entering, is a war zone, continue reading.)

Ask yourself or someone currently working in the organization the following questions:

1. Do you feel like crying when you enter your office? If so, how many times a week does this occur? When you walk out of your office, does this feeling leave you? (Note: Due to early programming against crying, this will not be an accurate indicator for most men. Find a woman who works in the same environment and ask her this question.)

2. Do you feel like punching your fist through the wall of your office? How often does this feeling occur, and do you know any other people at the worksite who are having this same experience? Note: Due to early and late messages of what constitutes ladylike behavior (socialization), this probably will not be an accurate indicator of most women's frustration. Ask a man these questions. Another method is to look around the workplace at the faces of the men employed there and count how many of them look as though they feel like putting their fists through the wall, and how many look as though they have already punched out a wall that day. Add these two numbers together and multiply by four. (This last operation is necessary due to men's socialization and continuing cultural practice of hiding their real feelings.)

If you have determined that you are working in a war zone, continue now to the next checklist.

How to Be Self-Caring While Working in a War Zone

1. First of all, realize—and never lose sight of the fact—that a war zone is where you are!

2. Set aside some specific time each day to plan your escape.

3. Take some time out each day to escape in your mind. Create pictures of peace and tranquility and nourish feelings of calm and serenity.

4. Move slowly and cautiously, and watch where you stand and step. Land mines are always hidden, and those left over from prior wars may be a surprise even to those who planted them. Do not carry secret messages from one camp to another. This assumes you can tell who belongs to which army when everyone is dressed in civilian clothes. To be safe, do not carry or send any secret messages since intelligence, counterintelligence, and counter-counterintelligence operations are growth industries in war zones.

5. Develop connections with persons outside the war zone and with persons like yourself who work inside. Together create peace and tranquility as described above, and nourish and support one another. Only in extreme circumstances should you talk about the war, the soldiers, and their tactics or weapons.

6. In case you and your friends and colleagues have violated the above, perform a cleansing ritual. Forgive each other for increasing one another's pain. Then arrange to view a funny movie together on the computer of whichever one of you has the biggest screen.

7. Should you or one of your friends get emotionally shot, observe the following steps in CPR (career-personality-rescue), otherwise the resulting wound to brain, personhood, and future life/work may be terminal.

a) The first thing to do after you've been shot is to keep moving. You may be able to make it out of the war zone under cover of the cross-fire.

b) Remove the bullet! As obvious as this step appears, many people have not done this. They have not allowed their wounds to heal. Present wars in work organizations often result when victims of prior wars do not remove old bullets and shrapnel.

c) The removing of the bullet must be done in the presence of persons not involved in the war, or at the very least, in the presence of persons not afraid of blood, sweat, and tears. (As you may remember from watching reruns of the television show M.A.S.H., people who fire weapons on other humans are, by definition, afraid of blood, sweat, and tears.)

d) Another tip from M.A.S.H.—go ahead and bleed, sweat, and cry as long as you are not in the presence of enemies, for these biological responses are healthy and will aid in your healing.

8. Do not hurt or blame yourself for being in the war zone in the first place, for being wounded in the war (if that has been the case), or for bleeding from that wound. A great part of the world of work operates as a war zone. Although the war has not spread world-wide as yet, to find a work setting that is peaceful is more unusual than to find a government that spends no money on weapons.

9. Do not be surprised if some of your former friends and coworkers who must stay behind in the war zone are afraid to be seen with you. War zones, by their nature, operate with either/or battle slogans such as, "Whose side are you on, anyhow?" "All's fair in love and war," "If you aren't for me, you're against me!" and other such paranoid delusions. Don't play, even if it means losing some of your favorite playmates.

Some Far-Reaching Solutions

After you have checked out the above possibilities and made some of the changes in your physical environment suggested in the previous chapter, you may need to consider more far-reaching solutions for taking care of yourself in the workplace. Self-care in the workplace is difficult (if not impossible) to maintain if you find yourself in certain types of situations. When your work is not having an effective outcome in spite of your best efforts, you are robbed of the good feelings that come from a job well done. Your workdays begin to feel as if you are rolling a large rock up a great hill, only to have it roll back down on you again. When you step back from the situation, you realize that the problems are not yours personally; they are at the level of the system. Here, the solutions are beyond what you can work out by yourself.

In some situations you can do your work and see an effective outcome, but in following the procedures and requirements of the job, you injure yourself, your coworkers, or the people you are trying to serve. In these situations, self-care requires that changes be made in the system regarding how the job gets done, how it is funded, or how the caregivers and clients are treated in the process. Again, you are beyond what you can work out by yourself.

It's helpful to remember that performing the role of caregiver, whether professionally or personally, frequently leads to recognition of the need for change at the system level. It's one thing to read about society's problems; it's another to deal with human needs closely and on a daily basis.

Sometimes, this recognition of needs is overwhelming to the caregiver. Then, self-care for a "giver who cares" involves moving out beyond the immediate and personal to a larger arena. It definitely involves using *Partnership Power*, as in the following examples:

- My friend Rose and her husband, parents of a daughter with mental disabilities, are appalled by the lack of services for persons who are mentally disabled in their state. They join other parents and, visiting other states, begin identifying qualities of desirable programs. They form an organization and, through this vehicle, advocate for increased funds and services at the state and national level. What they create together becomes a model for the nation.
- Teachers and social workers providing services to pregnant teenagers identify the need for drug and alcohol education and treatment to prevent babies being born prematurely and addicted. The caregivers design a program and approach their local United Way organization for funding.
- Human service workers in a rural community, while continuing their own graduate education through a university extension program, identify a problem in the way local agencies serve (or fail to serve) minority persons. With assistance from their university professors and members of the minority communities, the caregivers write and carry out a grant that helps them develop a human service system that works better for all clients.
- A mother loses a child when the child is killed by a drunk driver. With other families in the same situation she forms an organization to lobby for more stringent laws and stronger enforcement in order to keep drunk drivers off the road. Public information campaigns help to enlighten communities so they no longer tolerate people driving while intoxicated.
- Parents of the children killed at Sandy Hook Elementary School honor their children by starting a foundation to lobby legislators to keep guns away from people that shouldn't have them.

Stories such as these could fill many volumes, as could the stories of caregivers in similar situations who were unable to transform their own pain. Some "givers who care" felt their situation hopeless and they became overwhelmed and unable to take action on their own or others' behalf. Others attempted to change their world without fully realizing what they were up against, and in the process, didn't take the proper precautions to take care of themselves. In order to deal with the natural result of being a caregiver—our enlightened understanding of how organizations and policies need to change in order to better meet human needs—we need a clearer understanding of how large systems work and how change can occur in them. I offer the following models for bringing about change and taking care of yourself in the process.

Creating Change at the System Level

As you contemplate change at the system level, keep in mind that the dance of self-care is not a solo or even a simple duet. Choreographing even small changes in large systems requires a cast of hundreds, including plenty of support from a larger audience. In addition, you must be extremely clear about what role you are playing from which position, and on what stage. Some maneuvers need to be accomplished from behind the scenes or in the wings, others from the next county, but always with a chorus of support. As my community organizer friend Rose taught me, "You can get a lot accomplished if you don't care who gets credit for it."

No matter how gracefully introduced, any kind of change can generate a reaction of fear. And when money is involved, which is the most likely situation, people move into their survival mode instinctively. Some scenarios of change use the fear generated by a threat of taking money out of an organization to motivate people in the organization to allow particular changes to occur.

"Taking Money Out" Solutions

Though it may seem to you like scrip (paper money) in a Monopoly game, people in positions of power in large organizations become deadly serious about money coming into or out of their budgets. Care-giving helper-types often avoid the Taking Money Out alternatives, since the principal motivation is fear, not the preferred doing the right thing. But the fear of fines, reprisals, or lawsuits can move people to do the right thing. Then they can discover that this new way of being is a reward in itself. Given the opportunity, people often come to realize how much fun it is to live and work in a garden where people and projects are busy blooming. Let's look at three scenarios that use the threat of taking money out of the organization.

It's the Law!

In this scenario, the first step is to get a law, policy, or regulation enacted. Then quickly, while people still believe that the law will be enforced, help them to adhere to its requirements. Optimistically, this new way of doing things will be rewarding for everyone, and they will wonder how they ever got along in the old way. Working as a consultant to educators in school districts in Nebraska, I saw this solution work quickly and effectively.

> In the mid-seventies, a small change was made in the language of the laws governing the operation of schools that received federal funds. Title IX stated that no school could discriminate on the basis of sex in any of their educational programs or policies.[1] The initial effect was not on classroom schedules, textbooks, or teacher's salaries, though these issues were raised. The toughest question was "How can we have educational equity when we only have one gym?" Coaches and gym teachers spent many sleepless nights developing elaborate ways to give the girls access to the gymnasium for their sports without interfering with the boys' sports schedule.
>
> One school superintendent, the father of four daughters, easily saw the situation from the girls' perspective, which helped him understand the intent of the new law. He turned down proposals

that gave the girls the gym between 5 and 7 a.m. before school and on Sundays during church services.

"Let's put it this way," he said; "The girls can have the gym Monday, Wednesday, and Friday after school one week, and then after school Tuesday and Thursday the following week. Or, the girls and boys can alternate the use of the gym after school; one week the boys have it, the next week it's the girls' turn. Or we can do it this way: The girls can have the gym all to themselves for the next 50 years, since the boys have had it totally to themselves for the last 50!"

So, since nobody could figure out how to prevent it, the girls were given the opportunity to play sports. The outcome of this experiment is obvious to us now. Girls liked to play sports just like their brothers and gained the same value from the experience that boys had always gained. (They developed healthy bodies and strong minds and practiced being team players.) As it turned out, many parents had daughters as well as sons, and they came to the games and supported the school for their daughters' sake, just as they had done for their sons. And people discovered that the honor of the school, the village or town, and the state could be defended by the girls as well as by the boys. It became just as much fun for "our girls to beat their girls" as it was for "our boys to beat their boys."

Eventually, it became fun to "do the right thing." As one principal of a small school district said in response to being told what a good job his school had done opening opportunities for girls, "We are American citizens here," he exclaimed with considerable pride. "We obey the law!"[2]

Let's Strike!

A second scenario comes from the strategies of labor unions. Millions of workers in America have used collective bargaining and negotiations, sometimes involving the threat or actual use of strikes to achieve better working conditions, salaries, and other benefits. But we caregivers have shied away from these approaches, continuing quietly to provide services for others without thought for ourselves. This selfless "I'm not doing this for the money" attitude has resulted in caregivers appearing to be saps, and having the work they do less valued than occupations that demand higher pay. On those rare occasions when caregivers have used collective bargaining and negotiation (teachers and nurses striking, for example), the results have often been improvements in service. Smaller classroom size, while improving working conditions for teachers, also means each child can receive more attention from her or his teacher. Higher pay for nurses encourages more young people to consider a nursing career and alleviates the shortage of nurses. Increased pay for social workers means that these professional master's level college graduates don't have to receive food stamp assistance or work two jobs to feed their own children.

A self-caring approach to these issues is for everyone to win, but those who live in the power-over-others model don't always view it that way. There is great danger that the people in power will regard your interest in improving services and in taking care of yourself as a declaration of war. You would then be working in a war zone with only one move left: to plan your immediate escape.

On the other hand, it may be possible to bargain and negotiate changes that benefit you, your colleagues, and your clients without starting a war. You will need to sing the song of your request in the largest chorus you can organize. Enlist singers from outside the organization to perform featured solo roles, highlighting the beauty and wisdom of your choir's major themes. Finally, connect up all of this with everyone's funny bone, so that even if the situation becomes hopeless, it will not be considered too serious.

My Lawyer Can Beat Up Your Lawyer

The third scenario in the Taking Money Out solution involves litigation or the threat of litigation. This strategy can be combined with the other versions of taking money out mentioned above. Civil rights activists, for example, employed collective action by disobeying the law in order to get unjust laws changed. This was frequently combined with a class action lawsuit filed on behalf of all the people affected by an organization's policies or practices.

WARNING: Due to the tendency of organizations to move quickly from a garden-like state to a state of war, litigation and threat of same should be done only from outside the organization, preferably from outside the state or territory involved. This way, progress in human consciousness can occur without the sacrifice and painful death of the person who first thinks up or stands up for each new just idea.

Further Tips

- Taking Money Out solutions do not represent quick fixes unless the organization, through its risk management department, decides it is the right thing to avoid expensive court costs. Settling out of court will still probably mean that if you are the person who started all of this you need to leave the organization. You will be seen as a troublemaker, even by many of the people who are benefiting from the changes you helped to bring about. You will get satisfaction only if you are able to see yourself, as Bernie Siegel suggests, "as being used for a purpose, recognized by yourself, as mighty."

- If you and your friends get involved in a court case as a way of taking money out to educate the organization, you must plan on living an unusually long life. This will be necessary in order to find out how the court case turns out. Usually by the time these cases come to a hearing, few living persons on either side have any memory, personally (or through family oral histories and genealogies), of what a case was about.[3]

- If the people in the organization respond to your Taking Money Out solution as a declaration of war (and this is highly likely), do not be surprised by the treachery that will likely follow. As a caring helper-type, you will be ever aware of the importance of relationships and the connection of all living things. It is hard for you to fathom the potential wartime posture and attitude that can be ignited at a seemingly small provocation. This "All bets are off, never mind what I said yesterday / All's fair in war / Get them before you get gotten" attitude creates, at the very least, extreme confusion. The fact that you do not feel that what you have done is an act of war, either declared or undeclared, does not mean that the other folks are not defining the situation as such.

- Some experts feel that the move to define differences of opinion as acts of war is merely an excuse for some "power-over" types to justify stepping outside the bounds of human decency. This no-holds-barred approach means that the rulebook is out the window, no referee is present for the contest, and you must run (not walk) to the nearest place of shelter. Do not regard leaving the field as an act of cowardice but rather as an act of loving self-care. Remember, saving one's face while losing the rest of one's body or mind is no victory at all.

"Preventing Money Being Taken Out" Solutions

In the following story you will see how sometimes, just keeping the programs and funds we have can be a glorious victory for "givers who care." This strategy downplays the role of fear, although elected officials are always aware of the upcoming election and the voters they must be accountable to.

A Peaceful Piece of the Pie

Once upon a time a particular state legislature was facing a particularly serious budget deficit. Having at one time done the right thing for education, roads, and welfare services, they were casting about for places to cut spending rather than raise revenue. Most politicians are convinced that if they raise taxes, they lower the boom on their own political careers. So remember, they need lots of help to avoid an overwhelming fear of their own annihilation while they are doing the right thing.

Among the programs and items the legislature had slated for elimination were three advocacy organizations—the Mexican American, Native American, and Women's Commissions. Although these programs were small and cutting them wouldn't save the state very much money, they were seen as easy targets since they were run by caring helper-types for the benefit of people who had little power or influence in the first place.

A peaceful campaign was organized involving as many people from both inside and outside the organizations as possible. They were to sing the song "Save the Commissions" to the tune of "Give Me Some Men Who Are Stout-Hearted Men." The women from all three commissions did what women of all cultures do when the going gets tough. They went immediately to their kitchens and began baking. On the morning of the final deliberations, in the great hall where all great deliberations take place, on each legislator's desk was an appetizing pie. In the center of each pie was a fork with a small flag attached. The message on the flags read: "We don't want the whole pie; we're just asking for our own little piece, one-tenth of one percent of the state budget. Fork it over, fellas!"

And the people of the land won, living to fight peacefully another day. Truth, Justice, and the American Way demand an ever-continuing and ever-expanding sense of vigilance, along with a continually developing sense of humor.

So much for Taking Money Out or Preventing Money From Being Taken Out solutions. In the Monopoly game of making changes in large organizations, you might consider the positive strategies of bringing money into the organization.

"Bringing Money In" Solutions

Let's say you have some great ideas about how services could be improved in your organization. Nobody has any problem with the idea; there just aren't enough resources, especially money, to carry it out. Here is where the Bringing Money In solutions can be helpful. Included among these solutions are such strategies as writing grants for special projects, raising funds from sources that don't normally contribute to your organization, or designing ways for the organization to make money and/or receive prestige from something that means doing the right thing.

The latest in fundraising includes crowdsourcing and getting individual donations from free online platforms like Go Fund Me for one-time projects, or the platform Patron for sustained funding for artists and creators.

Fallacies in the "Bringing Money In" Solutions

The Bringing Money In approach to change in an organization is not as dangerous to your personhood or job tenure as the Taking Money Out scenarios. But there are fallacies that can interfere with your being able to use Bringing Money In solutions.

Fallacy 1: People in the organization must salute and pledge allegiance to the goals of your projects in order for the project to be successful.

As we saw in the Taking Money Out solutions, people may not understand or realize how satisfying it is going to be to help the sick, wounded, and needy or to eliminate, through preventive programs, the need for such help. If the people who run your organization had the same awareness you have, there probably would be no need for you to come up with your ideas in the first place. The world itself would be a significantly different place. The best you can hope for is that people in your organization will ignore you benignly and let you work to accomplish your goals.

Fallacy 2: People at the top need to have your value system in order for the projects to work out.

Just like the politicians who want to be reelected, your bosses want to hold on to their positions, enhance their reputations, and bloom where they are planted. If what you want to do can be seen as meeting their goals, you have a chance, especially if you are bringing in or generating the money yourself. In the beginning it helps if the source of the money brings with it some prestige for your boss and/or organization. One way to remember this is that "some money is gold, not just the usual green stuff." People and organizations that give away money (Fancy Friends From Afar) know this, and you need to proceed with caution so as not to be hurt by their good intentions. Outside funding sources have a tendency to underfund with the green stuff, relying on the "golden halo" effect of their money to open doors for the project. Level with your Friends From Afar about what you are really up against in your organization. Otherwise the demonstration project ends up demonstrating what a lot of people have been thinking all along—It's better to keep things the way they are.

Fallacy 3: Your organization's commitment to the changes will endure after the money is no longer coming in.

Enduring commitment is the best-case scenario, but it is improbable if the project has been of short duration. Also, the loss of funds may be interpreted as a loss of face by the organization's leaders. People in organizations can become what they do, but only if they are kept saluting, pledging allegiance, and applauding doing the right thing long enough for the memory traces to take hold in their bodies and minds.

"Not One Red Cent" Solution

This fourth type of solution to becoming and remaining self-caring while making changes in large organizations, I have called the "Not One Red Cent" solution. In this scenario you spend time in a work organization, learning all you can from the experiences provided. You take special precautions, in the best self-caring tradition, to avoid being fatally wounded in war zones. You move up in the corporation as far as the system will allow. You learn all you can and then you leave, taking with you all that you have learned to set up your own organization. The real fun comes when you bid against your former organization as an independent contractor and you win the contract.

You can take pleasure in this solution for, not only are you now free to do your own right thing in your own caring-helper way, but you can delight in the fact that the organization that drove you out will get Not One Red Cent of the rewards you are now able to earn through your skills and abilities.

Moving On

Many caregivers get caught up in the treacherous maze of organizational politics. Feeling that our cause is just, our values are right, or that the need is so great, we forget to protect ourselves so that we may live to fight another day. Like Julie, the mental health professional who worked 60 hours a week, we need to realize it is OK to save ourselves. And saving ourselves involves recognizing the true reality of what we are up against.

Consult with your "cuddle group" or "cave buds" and other support persons, both inside and outside your organization, to be sure you are seeing the situation with clarity. Determine whether the scenarios described above for making changes in your organization are feasible in your situation. If making changes is not feasible (and you have done what you can to get people in the organization to address the issues), perhaps the time for letting go of your work situation has arrived. You need to let go of your work situation if the following conditions exist in your workplace:

- The person in direct line of authority over you is an addict and is making work decisions out of his or her disease. (Your boss is a practicing alcoholic or workaholic or sex addict and expecting everyone who works for him or her to do and see things as your boss does.)

- You are given an impossible job without the resources to accomplish it. (Funding or staff levels are so low you have determined you are doing more harm than good to yourself and/or your clients.)

- The organization has changed priorities, moving away from the mission and function of your job. (You find it too painful to stand by and watch your project be dismantled.)

- You are being required to go against your own core values. (Helping people to stay in damaging situations creates internal stress for you.)

- The meaning of your life can be lived only by moving on to your next work challenge. Sometimes we outgrow our jobs. Even if we work in a healthy organization, the right step in our own self-care can be letting go without malice or rejection. Bless and release!

Letting go of a job can be as difficult as letting go of anything else we put our hearts and minds into. Most of us rely on our jobs for financial security and physical survival, not to mention meeting our needs for achievement and self-expression. This codependence on our jobs means that we need a lot of help to be able to be self-caring and self-healing in the workplace.

Sometimes moving away from a work situation that does not allow for us to meet our own needs for self-care means staying optimistic and faithful to the values we hold, realizing that they are connected to something greater than ourselves. We are not isolated voices in the wilderness when we experience support and connection from like-minded friends.

A support group that I found especially helpful years ago was one based on the twelve steps of Alcoholics Anonymous, Codependents Anonymous for Helping Professionals (CODAHP). We started one of these groups at our clinic to assist ourselves and other people whose jobs involve helping and serving others, with our own self-care. Though I could find no evidence online that this organization is still around as a separate organization, it's still possible to start your own group using the principles of Codependents Anonymous (CODA). Like all groups based on the twelve steps, it helps members recognize their powerlessness to control others and encourages a perspective that includes a relationship to a Higher Power or a force greater than ourselves.[4] Whatever resources you choose, whatever scenarios of change you decide to pursue—keep reminding yourself of the following:

I am as valuable as any and all of my projects and accomplishments, and as such I am deserving of having my needs met as I perform my life's work.

A time to weep and a time to laugh,
a time to mourn and a time to dance.

–Ecclesiastes 3:4

Self-Care and Our Home Life

In the sense in which a man can ever be said to be at home in the world, he is at home not through dominating, or explaining, or appreciating, but through caring and being cared for.

–Milton Mayeroff, *On Caring*

As the sun fades slowly in the West, the end of another workday is at hand. Following your footsteps down the hall to the street, the Muzak melody strums, "Oh, give me a home where the buffalo roam . . ." You begin to sing along, ". . . where seldom is heard a discouraging word, and the sky is not cloudy all day." That's entertainment, but it's not even remotely connected to the reality of most caregivers' lives. The following list describes scenes that may be a bit more familiar.

- You haven't seen the sun in weeks, and that's not because it's the rainy season in Seattle. Since your job involves serving others, you must be available to them when they want you. Many clients, patients, and customers want services before or after their own workday. Of course, their wish is your command, so you are available before the sun is up and long after the sun has gone down.

- There is no such thing as being off duty. Your about-to-vibrate smart phone is in your pocket and you know that at any time of the day or night your life may be interrupted. Like a cowboy on night watch, you rest and try to sleep with one ear attuned to the coyote's howl.

- You go home, but you carry your not-so-light briefcase or back-pack, full of paperwork that needs to be done before dawn. Your family has more than a few discouraging words to say about your requests to be left alone or to be excused from household chores for the evening.

- You go home, leaving your work at work, and begin struggling through your second job on the home range. This "moonlight-ing" turns out to be a different arena for the same caring role.

- Or you can't go home because you are already there. After being the home caregiver all day, you now keep yourself from strangling the person you live with who is playing out one of the scenarios above.

There are many different versions of the caregivers' homecoming, but the themes are quite similar. Too much work and not enough play. Too much taking care of others and not enough time for oneself. What is the particular theme song that expresses your home lifestyle?

"As Long as They Need Me" ("I know where I must be.")
"All of Me" ("Why not take all of me?")
"Only the Lonely."
"Hard Day's Night" ("and I am working like . . .")
"Sixteen Tons" (". . . another day older and deeper in . . .")
"I'm late. I'm late" ("for a very important date.")
"One Call Away" (". . . Superman's got nothing on me.")
"Count on Me"
Here name your favorite: _____

Whatever your particular verse or chorus, for those of us who do caring work, protecting personal time while meeting family responsibilities provides the supreme challenge to our ability to take care of ourselves.

The Endlessness of a Caring Lifestyle

In our personal and family lives, those of us who do caring work for a living may feel that our work is never finished. There is no such thing as time out or time off, even for very good behavior. When we are operating from a selfless "don't think of yourself, do for others" frame of reference, we are in danger of burning out from too much of a good thing. In relating to family and friends, we are presented hourly with opportunities for losing ourselves in the clamor of others' needs. And having "given at the office," we may have little left to give ourselves as we respond to the demands of others at home.

Laura, a working mother with young children, describes it this way: "I have an image of myself as a bass cello with strings running up and down the front of me, from my head to my feet. Other people can't see the strings, and even I forget they are there. Only my children know about these magic strings. Whenever they want something from me, they just reach over near my heart and pluck a string. They know just which one will cause me to vibrate, which one will get the response they want from me."

Since it is part and parcel of our lifestyle to live in caring connection to others, we cannot hope to run out of relatives. When children grow up, parents grow old, and there are still plenty of people who will pluck our strings if we let them.

Valerie has raised four children. Now she comes home to her husband's mother, who has been living with them for the past year. "It was supposed to be temporary, but now I'm beginning to wonder if this is a permanent arrangement. Bill's mom came because she was recovering from hip surgery and couldn't stay alone. Just when she got over that, she got a case of the shingles. Now she's broken her ankle, and I'm afraid to go home from work and find out what's happened next. Bill travels a great deal, so most of the caregiving in this situation is falling to me. I'm truly sorry for all her misfortune, but she doesn't treat me well, and I wish she wouldn't take her misfortune out on me."

Building Boundaries

What are we to do about the difficult dilemma of taking care of ourselves in the face of myriad requests from those we love, from those who are depending on us? As family members, we need and rely on one another. But sometimes the burden of responsibility isn't shared evenly, according to each person's age and ability. Sometimes we overdo our doing for others, which interferes with their doing for themselves and developing their own self-care skills.

Self-care and self-healing in our families means that we each take responsibility for ourselves, creating strong boundaries between ourselves and those we love. Let's review the skills of self-care and look at them from a family perspective.

The first one, *Sorting and Separating*, means that each family member is seen as an individual. Children are not simply extensions of their parents but are encouraged to identify and express their own needs and wants. Parents are not just extensions of the families in which they grew up. Each partner in the marriage works to resolve her or his individual issues with the family of origin. Continuing the *Sorting and Separating* of individual and family issues from their current relationship enables the couple relationship to uniquely meet the needs of the two parents (architects) creating it.

As we relate to growing children, *Sorting and Separating* is a continuous process. We begin by doing everything for an infant and gradually through the years transfer responsibilities for self-care to the growing child. Since the way parents handle things has such a strong impact on children, we parents, particularly women, get in the habit of asking ourselves, when children have difficulties, "What have I done wrong?"

When one of my sons had difficulty learning to read I questioned whether I had nursed him too long or too little, whether I had prepared him properly for the birth of his younger brother, or whether I needed to help him more with his homework.

AUTHOR REFLECTIONS

Christine: My oldest daughter, Alex, suffers with anxiety, which came on especially strong at puberty. She had always been my child who didn't like transitions. When we had a good freshman 9th-grade year I was surprised and delighted. That year she started her day with orchestra, where she played the cello and then moved on to pottery before diving into core academic subjects. It was in her 10th-grade year that the wheels fell off the bus. That year her day started with AP world geography at 7:10 a.m. Alex was a smart student who started the year with a 4.0 GPA. She ended the year with a 2.9 and the decision to withdraw from public school. She was done.

In order to let us know she was done, completely, she quit turning anything in. She would get up and go to school and be physically present, but she had mentally and emotionally checked out. The teachers couldn't figure out what to do since she wasn't a discipline problem, and as her parents we were stumped, too. We had tried tutors, therapists, interventions, et cetera. We had to examine and reexamine what to do. What was the best choice in this situation? It was obvious our child was not thriving and her grades reflected that she was failing. We were more concerned with her withdrawing from normal activities and with our inability to reach her. The decision was made for her to come home and be homeschooled for the last two years of her high school career. We needed to find and reconnect with our daughter. ✺

This parental dedication is admirable, but we must continually *Sort and Separate* what rightly belongs to us regarding our children's behavior and guard against taking on what rightly belongs to the child, the school, or the community. *Letting Go and Surrendering* means allowing each family member to make her or his own mistakes, and hold his or her own opinions. *Letting Go* of control over others means not interfering with somebody else's business. Sometimes marriage partners have an unspoken (and, I believe, unhealthy) pact in which they attempt to take care of each other. This isn't just a division of labor in which one person performs certain chores like taking care of the cars or household finances while the other does the shopping or cooking. Most organizations, families included, need some division of labor. And in circumstances of illness or injury, we do need to be cared for until we can get back on our own feet. But when one able-bodied adult is taken care of by another, this is an act of boundary violation and interferes with that person's caring for him- or herself.

In considering the above statements, we are already moving to the third self-care skill, *Building and Using Partnership Power*. One of the most difficult experiences in life is to be in a relationship with someone you love who is not taking care of her- or himself. In fact, it is important to note here: Do not attempt to build *Partnership Power* with someone who is not committed to taking care of him- or herself. This would be similar to jumping into deep water to save someone who is drowning when you don't know how to swim. Nothing is gained when both people go down. Families can be mutual benefit societies only when all members are committed to taking care of themselves and assisting each other.

So, the power struggles we are all familiar with in families can be eliminated. Instead of Mom saying, "How can I get my son up early enough to get to school on time?" she says, "Son, how can I be helpful to you in *your* getting up early enough to get to school on time?"

Stepping Back to see the big picture and the relationship between parts is essential when we find ourselves getting caught in somebody else's business. As one mother whose daughter has had problems with drug addiction told me, "When I find the effects of my daughter's actions coming back on me, I'm standing too close. It's time to back up and get out of the way." And of course, depending on how self-destructive the daughter's behavior is, the mother may need to be in the next county for her own protection.

Self-care and self-healing in intimate relationships require that we step back and observe ourselves in the act of doing whatever it is we and other family members are doing. We are each a part of whatever pattern is going on, and we are *Exercising Choice* only if we can identify what we are doing. *Stepping Back* gives us the opportunity to gain this important perspective.

The ability to say *no* and *yes* in *Exercising Choice* grows out of the other skills. For Psyche and most caregivers, saying yes to ourselves and no to others takes practice and more than a little courage.

FRIENDS AND LOVERS: A HEALTHY PACT

So what does a healthy pact between adults look like? Consider the following:

I RECOGNIZE MY RIGHT AND RESPONSIBILITY
TO TAKE CARE OF MYSELF.

I RECOGNIZE AND RESPECT YOUR RIGHT AND
RESPONSIBILITY TO TAKE CARE OF YOURSELF.

I PLEDGE TO MAKE MY OWN SELF-CARE
A PRIORITY IN MY LIFE AND ASK THAT YOU MAKE
YOUR OWN SELF-CARE A PRIORITY IN YOURS.

I PLEDGE TO DO WHATEVER I CAN
TO ASSIST YOU IN TAKING CARE OF YOURSELF
AND ASK THAT YOU DO THE SAME FOR ME.

I PROMISE TO ASK FOR YOUR HELP IN MY TAKING CARE OF
MYSELF WHEN I FEEL THE NEED FOR SUCH HELP.
I WOULD LIKEYOU TO ASK FOR MY HELP
WHEN YOU FEEL THE NEED FOR IT.

WE BOTH UNDERSTAND THAT OUR RELATIONSHIP IS BASED
ON EACH OF US TAKING CARE OF OURSELVES.

WHEN EACH OF US ACTS OUT OF WHAT IS TRULY BEST FOR
US, IT RESULTS IN WHAT IS BEST FOR THE RELATIONSHIP
AND FOR EACH OF US AS INDIVIDUALS AS WELL.

Double and Triple Whammies[1]

Double and Triple Whammies are what I call the compounding of
misfortune when we aren't taking care of ourselves in relation to those
we love, or when we are too closely involved with someone who isn't
taking care of her- or himself. The effects of a slip, a fall, or a mistake
are doubled or tripled when family members are holding on to one
another too tightly. Do you recognize yourself and/or your family
members in the Double Whammies below?

LOVE/HATE
I love you more than life itself.
You hate yourself
for not being able to respond to me.
I am hurt by your mistreatment of yourself.
I provoke you to mistreat me instead.
You are hurt by seeing the hurt you inflict on me.

THE CHASE
You run from yourself.
I run after you.

You see yourself in me. You run further from me.
Now you are lost from yourself. And from me.

DESPAIR
You hurt me.
I think I must have done
something wrong
for you to hurt me so.
I take what you send out,
sharpen it as a dagger,
and run myself through.
You blame me for bleeding.
And I blame myself
for ever having loved,
for being vulnerable,
for having been born,
for being me.

Take some time to construct your own whammies. Here's how:

1. Begin with some behavior that you don't like in another person.
2. Add a line that describes your response.
3. And then a line for his or her response, until the entire pattern is complete.
4. You are on the right track if you notice that the pattern is a circle and begins to repeat itself.

Now go back and identify a place in the cycle where you can *Exercise Choice*. See what other self-care skills you can use: *Letting Go and Surrendering* as you give another back the responsibility for his or her own life; *Sorting and Separating* what is yours and what belongs to the other person; *Stepping Back* further, or getting some help (*Partnership Power*) from outside the family system.

Combining the Self-Care Skills

As important as each one of the skills of self-care is, they rarely are used in isolation. It can be nearly impossible, for example, to say no to someone in your personal life if you have not done your own *Sorting* work. And once caught in a power struggle, you may need some help (*Partnership Power*) in standing back for a clear perspective. And self-care can be nearly impossible if you have not healed from early conditioning about yourself and about how you are "supposed" to be in the world. Let's look now at an example of the interconnection of self-care skills with self-healing in a story of one woman's successful healing from her childhood traumas.

The Wave

Meet Joan, an attractive, slender woman in her early thirties. Professionally Joan had achieved success and a regional reputation in the human relations field with her writing, consulting, and training activities. But her personal life had become so difficult that she had come to dread time off, and often she overworked in order to avoid dealing with friends and family. Especially with male friends, Joan had difficulty knowing what she wanted and being able to stick with her own agenda in the face of a friend's requests. At the time we began her individual therapy, Joan was feeling torn between two male friends, both of whom seemed to want "all of her."

"When I am talking with Bob, even on the phone, I begin to feel trapped, like I'm suffocating." While Joan described her emotional symptoms, she gestured to her upper chest, indicating this as the place in her body where she felt the pressure. "The more he seems to be pressuring me to spend time with him, the more uncomfortable I feel. As time goes on, I lose touch with what I am feeling and so I don't stand up for what I want because I don't even know what that is."

Joan's healing work over several weeks helped her to develop a clearer awareness of what she did physically to inhibit her breathing and when this inhibition occurred in her relationships with her male friends. After stepping back and looking at her pattern, Joan told the women in her therapy group, "It seems crazy, but I feel like I have to respond to whoever needs me the most."

The women in the group nodded in recognition of Joan's discovery since they too were often unduly affected by other people's expression of need for them. Group members laughed and teased one another good-naturedly about this helping habit. As one woman put it, "This system could lead to developing some pretty pitiful friends, each vying for the neediest-of-the-week award."

Over a period of several months Joan endeavored to interrupt this "fright and flight" response she had whenever friends wanted something from her. Recognizing that everything is connected "physically, emotionally, mentally, and spiritually," Joan embarked on a multifaceted program for her own self-care and self-healing. She began taking lessons in karate even though she couldn't imagine hurting someone on purpose. She continued working in the group and individually with me as her therapist. In her imagination she practiced developing a relaxation response and relating to her friends from a place of comfort and centeredness within herself. And in her real life with friends, there were gains and improvements in her ability to sort out what she wanted from what others expected from her.

After nine months of concerted effort, Joan hit a place of deep discouragement. "I feel as though I've come so far in my healing, yet not far enough. It's almost like I'm afraid for things to go too well, like I'm waiting on the next wave of bad feelings to hit."

Picking up on Joan's metaphor, I said, "So, whenever you venture away from the beach and into the water, waves come along to push you back up on the shore?"

"Yes, and the more progress I make, the more violent the waves seem. I'm not sure I can stand up to them," Joan said with more than a touch of discouragement in her voice.

Joan lay on her back on the massage table for her Rubenfeld Synergy[2] session with me. Using the suggestions of my gentle touch and her own creative imagery, she moved quickly to a now familiar place of peace and rest.

"Where is that wave now?" I asked her.

"It feels like it's suspended over my head, waiting to come down on me when I least expect it," Joan said, gesturing above her right shoulder.

"So it sneaks up on you. Well, what does the wave want from you? What is it trying to say to you?" I asked.

Joan's face grew pale, and terror built in her eyes as she responded to the questions with strong emotion: "It says, 'You are bad! You are bad! You are bad!'"

In a voice of gentle indignation, I probed her "wave" further. "What did she do that is so bad? Does she get to know what she did, to know of what she is accused?"

Speaking as the wave, Joan answered in an accusing voice, "You don't meet the standards."

"Well, that's a different story," I said, expressing some excitement and relief. "Not meeting the standards? Is that it? Well, that's different. Do we get to know whose standards you aren't meeting? Just for the record?"

"The standards of my family, the Chaplin family standards!" Joan said with a look of surprise that the information came from her, as she did not know she knew it until that moment.

Joan's family had instilled in her many of the common messages that keep people from feeling good about themselves. Joan was given unrealistic standards, standards that would have been unrealistic whatever her age and skill level. Perfection was the minimum standard in the household where she grew up. She was expected to be perfect or at least to suppress her own needs and wants and "act like" she was perfect. She was expected to be strong and take care of her parents and always try to please the adults in her life.

In addition to all this, in her adult life, she felt the need to hurry through her days and weeks, continuing to try harder to meet these impossible standards and continuing to feel bad about herself for falling short of the mark. After her discovery of how these feelings and ideas were programmed into her system, Joan's next steps included sorting and examining which standards and traditions from her family of origin she wanted to continue to observe and live up to and which ones to let go of.

Freeing the energy and tension she was using to keep the "wave" at bay meant that her images in therapy changed along with her relationships in real life. A short time later she pictured herself swimming in deep, clear water and sending the following message to her male friends about the type of partnership power she wants in her close relationships:

> "I enjoy swimming with you, but I won't be holding you up any more! I plan to be swimming in deep water far from shore. I'd rather swim alone than swim in the deep with someone who isn't a strong swimmer and cannot hold his own when the water is over his head!"

Developing Your Own Standards

Many caregivers have been given messages similar to Joan's. Do you have some or all of the following? "Be Perfect!" "Be Strong!" "Try Harder!" "Please others!" And "Hurry up!" (in complying with all the other messages).[3] Becoming a self-caring person means we must undo or redo these messages. And it's helpful to get hints from others about how they have become comfortable with their home lives.

Caregivers' Creative Solutions

Marie, a social worker and agency executive told me, "I'm pretty greedy for life, so I knew if I wanted to have it all, I'd have to get some help. My husband and I are quite a team, and we've been training our two kids to be a part of the team as well."

"Taking turns," "teamwork," and "cooperation" were frequently used expressions I heard when interviewing successful career women who also felt some measure of satisfaction with their home lives.

"We all pitch in and clean the house on Saturday mornings, and then we can go to a movie or do something else fun in the afternoon," Coleen, a bank teller told me. "Before we organized things in this way, I dreaded facing the weekend and all I had to do at home, while my colleagues who didn't have children were celebrating 'Thank Goodness It's Friday.'"

Getting meals on the table presented the most challenging family task and also the most creative solutions from the women I interviewed.

When Karen, a policewoman, married her second husband, combining her two children with his three, she reported nearly "coming unglued" until they figured out a strategy for mealtime. "My husband works at a treatment center, and we borrowed the system used there. We held a "community meeting" to plan and carry out a system that would be fair to everybody in the family, instead of having me do it all, which was my first approach. Now my husband and I each cook dinner one night a week. Each of the older kids takes a night, and we have one night we call "sandwich night," when the younger kids are in charge. One night is fast food night, so this makes it all manageable. Each cook takes responsibility for planning his or her own meals and making sure the supplies they need get on the grocery list. Now there's time for me to relax in the evening and even help the kids with their homework."

A "casserole co-op" was another creative strategy I heard about. In this model, three families each make one special meal over the weekend. They triple the recipe, and on Monday the families trade the extra portions with each other. In order for this to work, family size needs to be fairly comparable and food allergies and preferences similar. It's a great way to get your kitchen labor to go farther and come back to you with an extra measure.

I gleaned some additional suggestions from the women for taking care of themselves in their home places.

"Lower your standards," advised Shirley. "When we expect our homes to be perfectly tidy and perfectly clean we set ourselves up to feel bad about ourselves most of the time. Or if we do achieve these unreal standards, the quality of our family life suffers because everybody feels afraid to really live in the house."

"'Simplify! Simplify!' is my motto," Helen, a minister, said. "I ask myself, 'Do I need these clothes, these extra utensils? What can I eliminate so I won't have to take care of it or find a place for it?' Seems like at first we own things, and then, if we're not careful, our things own us."

"One of my favorite strategies for taking care of myself at home is to celebrate often," said Lois, the mother of three. "Being together as a family isn't just about getting the work done and getting the kids to do their homework. What I remember from my childhood were the fun times, the celebrations, the rituals of birthdays and holidays, and planning vacations. If we're overdoing work, whether at home or at the office, we don't have time or energy for these joyful events."

The Importance of Friends

Family members, with the exception of spouses, are in our lives by chance and not by choice. Relatives are thrust upon us by the circumstances of our birth, while friends are a different matter. Friends are freely chosen and can be some of the greatest resources for our own self-care. Since they want what is truly best for us, friends encourage and assist us in taking care of ourselves. Friends don't expect us to be perfect, and, seeing our wounds, they offer encouragement for our healing. Friends believe in us through times of self-doubt. They offer friendly support when the world seems unfriendly. Friends appreciate the honor of being a friend and celebrate our friendship as a gift to their lives.

Some people are fortunate to be able to continue the friendships of their childhood and youth into their adult lives, but most of us have moved far away (either physically, mentally, or emotionally) from early relationships. And many of us are too busy with our caring, helping responsibilities at work and at home to nurture and develop true adult friendships. Circumstances in our current culture have not made it easy to locate persons who are good candidates for friendships.

AUTHOR REFLECTIONS

Christine: When I moved from Texas to Georgia in 2007 Facebook was relatively new. I jumped on the bandwagon because I thought it was an excellent way to keep in touch with friends and family miles away. It helps me remember birthdays, reach out to offer support when someone is hurting, and more. Facebook can be an incredible tool for all of these things and promote connection. But Facebook and the internet can also have a dark side and pose risks for mental health and self-care. It can lend itself to unhealthy comparisons, as people tend to post their "best" pictures of themselves and their lives. I've had clients and friends say that it makes them feel like a failure when they see cool things about other people's lives. Employers can now access social media, and people who share too much or alternative opinions can be in danger of discrimination. Teenagers have committed suicide over cyber-bullying. In the latest news, we are watching the unfolding of how Facebook was used as a tool by a foreign government to influence American elections with the propaganda of false and inflammatory news stories. I continue to use Facebook as a great tool of connection with friends I'm separated from by miles, and I use it as a networking tool to build new relationships. However, the best way to foster my friendships continues to be over a cup of tea and good conversation. So true friendships may be as difficult to find and develop as they ever were. ❊

Wanted: Grown-Up Friends

Song: "Where Have All the Grown-ups Gone?"
(sung to the tune of "Where Have All the Flowers Gone?")

Where have all the grown-ups gone? long time passing,
Where have all the grown-ups gone? long time ago.
Where have all the grown-ups gone?
*Gone to graveyards, everyone,
When will we ever learn?
When will we ever learn?

Subsequent verses:
- Climbed into bottles, everyone,
- Drowned in drugs, everyone,
- Lost in work, everyone,
- Consumed by electronic devices,
- Taking pills, everyone,
- Hooked on sex, everyone,
- Hiding in food, everyone,
- Addicted to their phones.

The Joy of True Grown-Up Friends

A number of years ago anthropologist Margaret Mead warned the world that there were too many children for the number of adults who were caring for them. As a person who cares, helps, and gives to others in your work life, and then repeats the same patterns in your home life, you would probably join me in telling Margaret, "It's worse than even you had predicted."

Members of my women's therapy groups through the years have agreed with Margaret as well, realizing that it's not just the number of real, genuine, bona fide children. Actually, they can be a true joy and relief from the pseudo-kids who have passed the age of legal majority without coming close to real adulthood. If you are a person who cares for others at work and home, you need friends in your off-duty life who are true grown-ups. Group members helped me to compile a list of questions to ask yourself about a prospective friend.

THE TEST FOR A TRUE GROWN-UP

1. Is this person big enough to come out and play with you? If the person needs permission from someone else (mother, father, or former spouse), then he or she is not grown-up enough for you. This also applies to persons who need drinks, drugs, and other chemicals in order to play and have a good time. They most definitely are not grown-up enough to be a true friend.

2. Is this person old enough to play alone and stay entertained when you are busy elsewhere? If you have to be the social director, travel agent, and hostess with the mostest for your friend, this person is not a true grown-up.

3. Can this person cross the street without holding on to your hand? This may sound funny, but lots of friendships are based on one person riding the other's energy and then complaining about the direction or speed of the trip. If your friend can't boil water, fill her or his own gas tank, or go to the store alone, this person is not grown-up enough for you. You need to find someone who is self-sufficient and someone who welcomes a person of good company like yourself.

4. Does this person still run away from home often? Most kids go through a stage where they threaten to run away from home, and some teenagers actually do it. This is difficult enough to deal with from a bona fide teenager. Don't put up with this for a minute from a supposed-to-be-adult friend. If this person goes through various periods of hot and cold, hide and seek, come

here / go away, you know that this person is not a true grown-up and is not able to be a true friend.

5. Does this person have to take long naps frequently (in front of the TV, perhaps) even when not really tired? One of the unmistakable marks of a true grown-up is the ability to stay awake for one's life, or at least for long stretches of it at a time.

6. Does this person insist on fighting over toys and territory and who's boss of the game? Does this person cry or throw a fit when losing the hand, or not getting his or her way? Does this person cheat when you're not looking? You need someone who is mature enough to play games fair and square, to be a gracious loser and winner. Even if your candidate for friendship learned how to be a team player as a child, this may not be enough. Grown-up games require creative invention and negotiation about rules, roles, and rewards.

7. Can this person tell the difference between fantasy and reality? Is the person brave enough to tell the truth to you and to her- or himself? Can the person be available to hear what is true for you? Is this person dedicated to discovering the truth in life situations or does he or she insist on playing "make-believe" and "let's pretend"? A rich fantasy life can be a valuable, creative resource but not when there is confusion or mislabeling of what is fantasy and what is reality. People who lie for convenience or say to others what they think others want to hear are not candidates for true friends, and not likely to become so any time soon.

8. Can this person identify and ask for what she or he needs? Can this person behave gracefully when you are unable to meet the person's requests? Infants and young children express their needs by crying, screaming, or looking miserable. Adults, then, use clever detective skills to find out what is really wrong and what might remedy the situation. If your friend is not able to identify and communicate his or her needs and accept

disappointments gracefully a good deal of the time, this person is not a true grown-up.

In summary: Children, clients, patients, students, and even, in some instances, employees, may be people with potential. However, friends, spouses, and life partners must be capable of participating fully in equal partnerships. For you to experience this empowering opportunity, you must find people who are already true grown-ups. A good friend is someone who has already arrived at this place of responsibility. Good luck in using the above test to find friends who don't need you, and who don't need you to need them! One of the most important ways to take care of yourself, to be self-caring and self-healing is to

Give Yourself the Gift of Grown-Up Friends

Act Three

Practice and Rehearsal

The dancer is not separate from the dance, and all aspects of the dancer are needed for the dance. Each of the next four chapters focuses on one of the four dimensions of the self. Like weight, height, and depth, our physical, mental, emotional, and spiritual aspects together describe a consistent whole. Like colors and shapes in a kaleidoscope, turned slightly, you highlight a particular pattern; turned again, the material rearranges into a different pattern.

Part of our need to heal comes from our culture's division of these dimensions into separate, unrelated domains presided over by isolated, often warring experts. Physicians and physical trainers have claimed the physical; professors and scientists, the mental; various mental health therapists, the emotional; and ministers and priests, the spiritual. Like children playing king of the hill, each expert claims to be the most important one.

Even within ourselves the dimensions may seem to be competing for our time and attention. The dance of self-healing involves reclaiming one's inner authority over all of the dimensions of the self. Experts can be useful, but they should work for us. The dance of self-caring involves a balanced relationship between all the dimensions. As we look at the dimensions individually, let's keep in mind their connections to one another.

Self-care isn't possible without slowing down physically, quieting the mind mentally, allowing ourselves to experience and move through feelings emotionally, and coming to realize spiritually that in the still-point, order will emerge out of what appears to be chaos.

Allow yourself to trust joy and embrace it.
You will find you dance with everything.
–Ralph Waldo Emmerson

Reclaiming and Reconditioning: The Physical

*Like putty, we are either shaping ourselves
or we are drooping; like clay, we either keep ourselves
moist and malleable or we are drying and hardening.*

–Deane Juhan, *Job's Body*[1]

"One, two, buckle my shoe. Three, four, touch the floor!" At one time most of us were able to stay physically fit through the fun and games of childhood pastimes. Jumping rope, running, riding bikes, climbing trees, we developed strength and stamina, flexibility, and the ability to rest at the end of a hard day's play.

As we put away the things of our childhood many of us lost the enjoyment of physical movement and the good feelings of experiencing our physical dimension. Staying physically fit (when we decide to care about it at all) becomes serious work.

"One, two! Buckle those shoes! Three, four! Touch the floor!" And the beat goes on! Burn, Burn! We do twenty of these and thirty of those and repeat to ourselves, "No pain, no gain!" Pushing our bodies a little farther, a little faster, we don't notice the muscle that says, "Enough!" And we forget to ask ourselves, what is all this fitness for? The baby-boomer generation was the first generation to embrace fitness. This changed how we viewed our bodies and our physical selves. At first we jumped right into exercise and fitness programs to stay healthy and young. It looked so easy on the video screen. But then, for many of us, came the injuries. As it turns out, enthusiasm and good intentions are not sufficient to insure a safe outcome.

Discouraged by overdoing, we then experienced periods of ignoring and denying our body's needs. We tell ourselves we "just aren't athletic," we "don't have time," or "What's the use?"

What does fitness in the physical dimension mean for people whose work involves caring for others? There are five aspects to physical fitness: stamina, strength, flexibility, cardiovascular fitness, and relaxation.[2] Stamina to marathon runners means being able to withstand a long race. Stamina for caregivers is about how much energy we have left over for our own lives after a long day at work.

Football players build strength to push back the line or to avoid being run over by a stronger team. Physical strength for caregivers may mean being able to repeatedly lift children or a sick elder without hurting oneself. Many caregivers, such as physical therapists, dentists, nurses, and beauticians, need strength to survive being constantly on their feet. And it takes strength to hold a particular body posture for long periods of time, bending over a client or patient.

In sports like tennis and racquetball, flexibility enables players to respond quickly in changing directions. Some caregivers risk losing their flexibility, as they sit for long periods of time listening to the needs of others. Doing paperwork and talking on the phone can be more of the same rigid thing. Like everything in the physical dimension, using our flexibility is the only way to keep from losing it.

In sports, cardiovascular fitness means the body is able to respond when a sudden demand is made on it and then to return quickly to a state of rest. Caregivers' hearts need these same abilities. Appreciating our needs in the physical dimension means recognizing that our hearts and lungs require more opportunities for vigorous activity than most of our job and home tasks provide.

For the athlete, relaxation is an ease of movement that comes from an efficient use of the body. Caregivers need such efficiency as well. Along with the ability to let go of the stresses of caring work, we need the ability to rest for recovery and renewal. It is too late when exhaustion or pain signals our need for rest. Self-care in the physical dimension means taking care of our needs before, or as, they arise. Like runners who are advised to keep drinking water during the race, by the time we experience thirst, the damage of dehydration has already begun.

Hazards of Ignoring Our Physical Selves

Meeting our needs in an early stage requires paying close attention to our physical selves, but our training at all levels of schooling has sent us in the opposite direction. As first graders we lined up for the bathroom when school schedules dictated rather than listening and responding to our own inner signals. As middle high students we learned to gulp down lunch for more time on the playground. And should we exhibit too much physical movement in class, we were barred from the playground until we could learn to "sit still."

High school and college found us losing sleep cramming for exams. Internships and training programs expected us to jump over the hurdles of long hours, little sleep, and an extended diet of junk food. As one physician participant in a workshop on self-care expressed it, "As a medical student you really can't take care of yourself. Interns hold their breath and 'gun it' through the training. Later, in practice, you try to find the shortcuts that make life bearable."

Think of the rituals involved in earning a professional degree or becoming licensed or certified for a particular field of work. Like fraternity pledges going through hazing, candidates pass the humiliation test and prove they can take what those in authority dish out. This sacrifice of our sensitivity and our self-care is rendered on behalf of learning or science, selling, or service, whatever seems the noblest of causes at the time.

What price do we pay for ignoring our own physical needs while living a caring-for-others lifestyle? We will look at three professional helpers and the particular physical difficulties they have encountered. We will see a caring lifestyle that consists of too little movement, one that contains too much, and a third that illustrates the danger in the way movements are performed.

The Case of the Transfixed Therapist

Meet Rex, a 68-year-old man who has been a psychotherapist for over 40 years. He sees 30 to 35 people each week, except in the month of August and the two weeks he takes off each January. He came to one of Ilana Rubenfeld's workshops on self-care for helping professionals, complaining of stiffness and pain in his neck. A physician who x-rayed him told him that he had arthritis. Rex had concluded that there wasn't much he could do about his discomfort, but he volunteered to show the workshop leader and group how he sits when he is working with his clients.

A mock office was set up at the workshop, and Rex pretended to be working with a client. Ilana suggested he imagine a particular client, one that he considered especially difficult to work with. As Rex continued to imagine listening to his difficult client, his posture changed dramatically. When he was talking to the leader and the group, he was sitting upright with his spine elongated. As soon as he imagined his difficult client he sunk into his habitual listening pose.

"Freeze right where you are!" Ilana directed. As though pushing the stop-action frame on the video recorder, Rex became a still statue of his listening habit.

"Exaggerate that position," she added, hoping to further heighten his awareness of the physicality of his listening habit. Rex's listening position meant that he was leaning forward, elbow on knee, sticking his neck out, chin on hand, somewhat reminiscent of the "thinker pose" of the famous statue. His eyes were focused straight ahead on the client. When asked to name this pose Rex exclaimed, "I'm trance-fixed!"

He was correct. From his fixed position he could not move easily to the right or left. The strain of hour by hour, year by year living in this position had cost him the loss of the rotational movement of his neck and spine. He felt stiffness and quite a bit of pain on occasion. He felt drained even before he got to the end of each workday. Even the simple act of driving his car had become a dangerous activity, since he could look only straight ahead.

The role that his mind was playing in all this became apparent when he was asked to experiment with listening to his clients from different positions. He explored postures that were less strenuous for him, sitting back in his chair, which meant moving farther away from the client. When a position felt physically comfortable for him, he worried it might give the wrong message to his clients. "I feel that they will think I am not listening to them, that I don't care about them or their problems," Rex said.

The leader invited Rex to experiment with listening to people from these more comfortable positions and postures as he interacted with people at the workshop. Since workshop participants weren't paying for his time like clients do, Rex was able to experiment with the more comfortable listening postures and get reactions from others as to how he came across.

After some experimentation, Rex began to loosen his fixed notions about how to be with others as a helping person. As he allowed more flexibility in his physical positions, he relaxed emotionally and mentally.

This allowed more aspects of him to show through to his colleagues at the workshop. The real test would come, of course, when he was back home listening to his real clients.[3]

The Importance of Posture

Improper posture is a most significant energy drainer in our daily lives. As we carry out the tasks of work and home life, the answer isn't just to "sit up straight" or "put your shoulders back" as most of us have been advised to do as children. Posture isn't a position. Posture is a relationship between all parts of our bodies as we engage in the movements of living. As Rex clearly demonstrated, our posture reflects our attitude about ourselves and others and our beliefs about what it takes to achieve what we are trying to accomplish.

Whatever techniques we have developed to accomplish actions such as sitting in a chair, walking, swinging a golf club, or brushing our teeth, we have achieved some level of proficiency. After years of practice we are unaware of what we are doing to accomplish these tasks, but, whatever it is, it feels natural and necessary. Many of these techniques, like Rex's listening posture, may be costing us our energy and good health in the long run.

Around the turn of the century, the Shakespearean actor F. M. Alexander discovered this truth when he developed laryngitis frequently as he practiced his acting craft. Since this was before the invention of public address systems, he might have just considered this illness an occupational hazard. Instead, he reasoned that there might be something in the way he was using his physical self that was creating the problems with his voice. Observing himself with mirrors from many angles (video cameras hadn't been invented yet), he became aware of what he was doing with his head and neck as he performed his dramatic work. He identified what he came to call his "misuse of self" in posture and movement, which inhibited his voice and created his frequent bouts with laryngitis.

Alexander also found that changing these unproductive habits was not as easy as it looked. He eventually developed the Alexander Technique, a system of psychophysical education that helps people learn to treat themselves more gently as they perform daily tasks.[4]

Practicing a New Posture

Remember, healthy posture is not a position but a relationship between parts that allows for ease of movement and a lack of strain. Try the following activity to get an understanding of the importance of Alexander's discovery.

1. Go through the motions of what you usually do at work, in slow motion.
2. At some point in the process, freeze.
3. Notice the fine detail of the position of your head and neck in space. (Is your chin jutting forward? Is your forehead reaching out beyond your chest?) The desired movement is for your head to move subtly back and up, so let's practice by starting with exaggerating the opposite.
4. Place one palm across your forehead and the other on the back of your neck. Move your chin forward and notice how your neck is shortened.
5. Move your forehead back and allow your chin to drop and the back of your neck to lengthen.
6. Grasp several hairs from the crown of your head and gently guide your head in an upward direction, lengthening the spine as you go.
7. Now perform your work tasks from this new posture and experience the lightness and ease of your movements.
8. Notice what old habits cause you to lose this new posture.
9. To reclaim your new posture repeat steps 4 through 6.

The Importance of Moderation

Besides posture and the problem of too little movement, a caring lifestyle can involve too much movement. Let's meet another caregiver who illustrates that type of problem.

Reverend Perpetual Motion

No disrespect intended. People call her Reverend Perpetual Motion—to her face! Dr. Karen Rutledge, a hospital chaplain, is the closest thing to a perpetual motion machine you'll ever see. She's up the stairs two at a time and down in a flash when her pager sounds its beep. Karen is 48, but you'd never know it. Her energy seems boundless. She appears to be working every shift, often coming back to the hospital on weekends and evenings. She grabs a hamburger on the run, and nobody can figure out when she sleeps.

"My job is supporting parents and staff through the difficult times in the treatment (and sometimes death) of the children who are our patients," Karen said. "It's a perfect job for me, though I didn't have this situation in mind when I went to the seminary. I thought at the time I would have my own church. But this assignment feels like real pastoral care. It brings together all my interests and skills from my years as a teacher, mother, and community volunteer. The only shadow on the horizon is that I have just discovered I have a health problem. When I was having trouble getting over the flu I went to the doctor, and he tells me I have had a mild heart attack. There is heart trouble in my family, but I didn't experience any warning signs. In the back of my mind, I knew I wasn't eating right or getting enough sleep, but I thought the good feelings I had from my job would carry me through."

Attending to Our Physical Selves

Our bodies cannot stay healthy when we tend to others and forget to attend to ourselves. As Julian Silverman suggests in his book *Health*

Care and Consciousness,[5] our habit of living in our heads doesn't allow us to be healthy. Our bodies cannot stay in balance without the energy that some degree of attention provides. As soon as we pay attention to our bodies, we begin to make a difference. This information that only the body can give helps us to know what we need, what to do next, and how to alter our course.

Because of our special sensitivity to others, we caregivers have to overcome a tendency to lose track of ourselves and our own needs while relating to others. Sometimes it would be quite accurate for us to hang a sign on our chests, the kind shopkeepers hang on their doors: "GONE FISHING!" or "NOBODY HOME!" or a special one for mothers, "BE BACK IN 20 YEARS!"

A physical illness is often the signal that gets our attention, and we start to get the message "We aren't invincible."

Karen's self-healing journey began when the doctor told her she had a heart condition. Her self-caring journey began when she stopped thinking of herself as a sprinter and began regarding herself as a long-distance runner.

Karen began to change her lifestyle systematically. Her first decision was to treat herself to a weekly therapeutic massage. Though this seemed self-indulgent to her at first, she soon realized that through the skilled touch of the body worker she was developing a consciousness about her body. As Deane Juhan describes it, "Touching hands are not like pharmaceuticals or scalpels. They are like flashlights in a darkened room. The medicine they administer is self-awareness."[6]

Growing out of Karen's emerging self-awareness of her body came a commitment to focus on what, how, and when she was eating. She joined forces with a nutritionist, and together they systematically looked at how her body was digesting and assimilating what she was eating. She learned that nourishment isn't just whether you can digest that hamburger; it is about what happens to the cells. Karen described her reactions to the process this way:

"At first hearing, I seldom welcome any suggestions made to me to alter my eating habits. Intellectually, I had dozens of excuses why the suggestion was too much trouble or wouldn't work. Emotionally, I felt threatened that I would be losing something important or trading something enjoyable for something distasteful. I achieved the best results through being willing to try a small change for a short period of time. As each small change produced a benefit in my system, I got the courage to try another."

DEVELOPING A HEALTHY RELATIONSHIP WITH FOOD

Here are some suggestions for moving towards a self-caring lifestyle as far as food and physical nourishment are concerned. Consider, as some clients have done, copying these suggestions and posting them on your refrigerator door.

1. Don't make dramatic or drastic changes in your diet, as this is stress-producing. Slow and steady adjustments are more likely to be maintained. Should you develop an adverse reaction to some dietary change, it's easier to identify the cause of the difficulty if alterations are introduced one at a time.

2. If your habit is to use food as your drug of choice to stuff unpleasant feelings or create positive ones, work with a therapist to learn healthy ways to handle feelings. Keep your food and dietary planning simple or you won't be able to stick with it. Shop for and prepare foods on the weekends so you can eat healthfully during your work week. A program like Weight Watchers can be helpful in reeducating yourself on what foods to eat and their portions.

3. If your plan is to lose weight or let go of your addictive foods, join a group such as Overeaters Anonymous for support.

4. Stay skeptical of "quick fixes" in the nutritional area as well as in other areas of your life.

5. When the time seems right, consider working with a nutritionist or a doctor who specializes in preventive medicine.

6. Begin substituting intermediate foods for unhealthy ones (cookies sweetened with fruit juice replacing cookies with sugar, decaf coffee or herb teas replacing caffeinated drinks).

7. Make breakfast your biggest meal (include protein) and supper your lightest (soup and salad). This pattern can be helpful also in getting a good night's sleep.

8. Help your elimination system by taking two glasses of water with lemon juice upon rising, followed by moderate exercise such as walking. This morning ritual flushes out toxins and gets the system ready for the day.

9. Develop other ways to comfort or nurture yourself physically besides using food. Consider leisurely hot baths, massages, and the gift of some quiet time.

10. Include exercise in your self-caring nutritional plan, since exercise plays an important part in helping your body use what you are feeding it.

11. Alter grandma's recipes in the direction of lower fat and less sugar so you and your family can still enjoy them.

12. Try out these healthy variations of old recipes when you bring food to the office for parties or coffee breaks. This way the culture of the office can become supportive of eating in a self-caring way.

13. Occasionally disobey the rules of whatever plan you design so that you don't become rigid, resentful, or arrogant.

14. Make a movement date with a friend, instead of a date to eat food. This could include going for a walk in the park or taking a yoga class together.

15. Listen to your body's wisdom. What foods work for your personal system? Become aware of which foods don't like you. Make sure food allergies are not impacting your health.

16. Begin or revive a ritual of expressing gratitude for the gift of good food before meals, even when eating alone. This can be as simple as a moment of attentive silence or as elaborate or formal as the prayers of grace recommended by your religious tradition.

The Importance of Balance

Our third professional helper illustrates what happens when not only do you do too much, but it is done too intensely and without the balance provided by other types of experiences. Marie's life had become all work. In addition to being a professional helper, she had been a student working part-time to finish her degree in psychology.

Marie the Magnificent

"I'm nearly 30 years old and this is my eighth year of going to school for this degree. After I finish this next round of tests I still have a dissertation to write and an internship to go through," Marie told me on her first visit to my office.

"I believe that stressful times can be opportunities for growth," Marie said, "but I am losing confidence that I can grow from these next few months of exams and faculty reviews." Marie was having trouble sleeping. Experiencing numbness in her fingers and tension headaches, she felt guilty whenever she took time from her studies. Having little time with her husband caused trouble in her marriage. Marie and I discussed her approach to achieving her educational goals. Her success was impressive—straight A grades, outstanding student awards, truly a magnificent record.

Overdoing had been her strategy. Doing "her best" meant studying "every waking moment," and this had worked for many years. But now, when the stakes were higher than ever, she was worn out. Angry at the price she had been paying, she felt unsure of herself and panicked at the idea of letting people down. And of course, she didn't want to destroy that superwoman image she had so carefully constructed throughout the years.

Marie's story hasn't ended yet. I suggested ways to become more self-caring. I introduced her to some ways to let up on herself, and ways to become aware of her physical self. She rejected any suggestion that she relax her lofty standards. She chose to continue pushing herself even harder to "get it over with."

"I'll start taking care of myself after I get my degree," she told me. Having been there myself and having observed many social work students make the same decision, I knew that after graduation, there would be a price to pay. Given the symptoms she was already experiencing, I expressed my hope that she not injure herself irreversibly in this process of achieving near perfection. I let the matter drop in the interest of my own self-care. I told her I would be available to work with her on her recovery when she felt ready to do so.

Reclaiming Our Physical Selves

Overdoing teaches many of us the necessity of taking care of ourselves. Bodies neglected for too long show disastrous results and suggest the necessity of reclaiming our bodies and learning to love them. Many people are dissatisfied with their bodies, wanting to be taller or thinner, or they disrespect their bodies' limitations. Maybe it's your thighs or chest that doesn't meet your expectations! The list is potentially endless, and the constant struggle puts us at odds with vital parts of ourselves. It is important to remember that our bodies are not only vehicles to transport our brains. Our bodies are a significant aspect of who we are, and appreciating, respecting, and loving our physical selves is a significant part of appreciating and loving ourselves. We have heard the stories of three caregivers and their experiences with the physical effects resulting from their work stress. For some additional help with this dimension, let's consult with the Soma Twins. Remember, she is sensory, he is motor, so they should have much to teach us about taking care of our physical selves.

The Soma Twins on the Stress Systems

I asked the twins to explain what it is that happens physically when people who care for others burn out. Touchy responded, "The importance of posture and how our mental attitude affects it was illustrated by Rex, the transfixed therapist. He was caught in the possum response—inactivity to the point of rigid stillness. This reaction is self-protection for a possum as he "plays dead" to fool his enemies, but it doesn't work for people. The stress of staying in one place habitually takes its toll in the loss of flexibility and range of movement, and the sensitivity to be in touch with your own needs."

Feelie added, "All the different stress responses are costly over the long haul. Overdoing, as Karen and Marie described, is costly when continued over extended periods of time. When the 'fight or flight' response of the sympathetic nervous system (arousal) goes on for too long, it depletes the body's resources and puts strain on major organs like the heart, liver, and lungs.

"If the parasympathetic nervous system (inhibition) is active for too long, the immune system becomes depressed, leading to susceptibility to a wide range of diseases, from mental depression to cancer.[7] Sometimes people feel drained and used up, yet like Marie they are unable to relax and replenish themselves. Others turn off, toughen up, and hold on to their tension. Like Rex, they can't express themselves, and they won't allow themselves to receive help from others. All of this places tremendous stress on the body."

Touchy described a remedy. "Two systems of the nervous system (sympathetic and parasympathetic) need to be in balance in order for people to experience health and well-being. Instead of thinking of relaxation as regulated by an on/off switch, picture a rheostat knob that allows you to brighten and dim the lights with a great deal of variety. If doing (action) and nondoing (relaxation) are operated by a rheostat knob, then each combination creates a particular body/mind state. For each task, activity, and skill there is an optimum body/mind state, and the possibilities for unique and creative combinations are infinite."

Feelie added: "When a person is able to relax (and there are different levels of this in the body), anything extraneous is deleted. When movement becomes a dance, only what is necessary to the movement is activated and only to the appropriate level."

Touchy concluded, "From the point of view of the stress systems, all elements of fitness rely on relaxation—the ability to release excess tension and inhibit unnecessary activity."

"Dancers and master athletes perfect their technique by developing the ability to sense small changes in balance, position in space, and breathing," said Feelie. "This kind of sensitivity isn't possible when there is excess tension or a bracing within the body. Caring people are already sensitive to others, so becoming self-caring means heightening our sensitivity to ourselves as well."

Movements for Mending

As any young child will tell you, being made to sit still is a punishment. Our need for movement is as powerful as our need for food and rest. Fortunately, children's games provide rich opportunities for different kinds of movement. Most kids wouldn't consider giving up moving unless, while playing hide-and-seek, the seeker comes too close to their hideout. Then they flatten down, suspend all movement including breathing (possum), and hope that they have escaped discovery. Once a child is discovered, that child will be "it" in the next round of play.

Like the children's game of "statues," changing the way we move and the position of our bodies in space provides us with an interesting escape from habitual ways of being in the world. Since everything is connected, moving our bodies means that we are freeing our minds as well. One of our favorite InterPlay forms is Shape and Stillness, which involves using a single hand or your whole body to alternate making shapes. In each shape you give yourself the gift of stillness.

You'll find more "Movements for Mending" in appendix A. Intersperse these activities into your daily schedule as a way to further develop your ability to relax, your flexibility, and your strength. And notice any difference this movement makes in your stamina at the end of the day. As you heighten your sensitivity to your own body, what is needed for balance becomes obvious, and balance is the essence of self-care.

Who is Your Inner Instructor?

How we treat ourselves in our inner world has been strongly affected by the teachers and coaches of our youth. You may be having trouble maintaining your sensitivity and staying in a self-caring attitude towards yourself due to the type of instructors you actually experienced. You may have met the dance instructor Madam Haughty Hanna. Not having taken care of herself as she aged, she now uses a cane that she pounds continuously on the floor.

She doesn't mind using the cane to poke at her students should they dare to make a mistake. Her special enjoyment is teaching by humiliation, ridiculing her students' physical characteristics, and attacking their personalities if they, even momentarily, seem to feel good about themselves.

Another damaging type of instructor or coach is one I call Hurly-Burly Harold. He and the others of his ilk are graduates of the Kick Butt School of Instruction and should be avoided at all costs. This cigar-smoking, pot-bellied weasel tells his team members that they played such a lousy first half they can't possibly win. He adds insults to his injury by making remarks about how they played like "girls, queers, and pansies!" (It is not clear why this particular flower is picked out for insult, but it seems to add fuel to his fire.)

Both of these instructors hope that the students' hatred of the one who mistreated them will motivate them to do the near impossible and prove their instructors wrong. When the athletes do win, or the dancers perform well, comments are made such as "How come it took you so long?" Students are also reminded that this just proves they could have performed well all along.

Another version of this type is the gym teacher who teaches his students how to hate physical activity and their own bodies as well. Punishment for misbehavior becomes laps around the gym or, better yet, around the school grounds. That way the kids can get sick from exposure to inclement weather and peers can witness their humiliation as well.

An Inner Instructor of Another Kind

In spite of the large number of Madam Haughty Hannas and Hurly-Burly Harolds, another type of instructor has been emerging on the scene in recent years. This teacher sees her job as the development of the inner dancer or athlete. Her philosophy is not that winning is everything, but rather that, everything that happens is a win. She instructs her students to repeat the following affirmation before each practice and each game or performance.

I am as important as any one or all of my projects, goals, and accomplishments—past, present, and future. I allow myself to be fully present to the task at hand, realizing that, whatever happens, I will learn from it.

This instructor, Ivy the Instiller, seeks to develop in her students a sense of attention and focus, and an attitude of discovery, an ability to make mistakes and learn from them, to allow confusion and sometimes not to know the answers. Most of all, Ivy insists her students learn how to play.

You might want to develop your own Inner Ivy. She's the kind of person who, when all of the members of the gymnastics team fell off the high bars during an important meet, fastened the following note to their dressing room door:

HEY, TEAM!
Falling is not a giant zap from the gods
meant to embarrass, humiliate, and hurt you,
but falling is one of the things that happens
in the process of "going for it," as you move
too close to your growing edge. It is a sign that
you have made an error and you need to
BREATHE..............as in keep breathing,
LAUGH...................as in keep releasing,
GET UP........as in keep moving,
LAUGH.......as in keep enjoying,
and get back on the horse,
ring, barre, or floor!
SMILE........as you uncover, discover,
recover the lessons of each particular fall.

AUTHOR REFLECTIONS

Sheila: This poem was inspired by an incident that occurred during a competition I observed while visiting my son Kevin, when he was a college gymnast. The lessons of this experience came in handy in 2014 when my feet stuck to the floor as I was moving sideways in my dance class. Unable to get my feet under me, I fell on my shoulder and broke it. In the nine months that followed, I learned how common falling is, especially as we grow older, and how much work it is to regain a full range of motion after a serious fall. Thanks to physical and massage therapists, Bollywood and Zumba dance classes, and my own determination to do the work assigned, I'm back nearly as good as new. A special thanks to the gymnasts for showing me that it's not what happens to us, it's how we react and respond. ❀

Christine: Our bodies have so much wisdom to share, if only we would listen; I for one am not always good at it! I became a long-distance runner at the age of twelve, when a coach I loved and admired told me to go run two miles, so I did. I was one of the only ones that finished. I wasn't fast, but I was determined. From that day on, until I graduated high school, I was a long-distance and cross-country runner for our track team.

Many years later, in the habit of ignoring my physical body as I took care of everyone else around me, I realized I was in trouble. As I approached my 40th birthday, I was pre-diabetic and needed something to change. I set a goal and trained for two years, then completed the first of several triathlons. I also got real with myself about my eating habits and what my body personally liked. I realized that I was sensitive to gluten and started eating more vegetables and protein and no gluten or dairy. For the first time in over 20 years I slept through the night! It is incredible how happy my body was when I listened. I had also realized over the years that exercise sometimes bored me, and one of my tricks to stay engaged was to have a fun and varied workout. My workouts often include yoga, walking, swimming, weight lifting, river running, biking, dancing, Zumba, and jogging. Over the years, I have noticed that six days a week of at least 20 minutes of exercise each day is my sweet spot and keeps me healthy, both physically and mentally. The other thing I know to be true is that it is vital that I take care of myself by meeting my physical needs in order to continue caring for others. ✽

SUMMARY

In living a self-caring lifestyle we are affected by habits of the past, beliefs we have about ourselves and about how others view us, and the feelings and attitudes we bring to the helping situation. The dance of self-care in the physical dimension involves . . .

Movement ———— affecting posture and attitude
which affects breathing ———— which affects energy
—resulting in becoming DRAINED or ENERGIZED

Those who dance are thought mad by those who hear not the music.

–Friedrich Nietzsche

Recalling and Revisioning: The Mental

The mind is the source of liberation as well as of bondage.
–The Upanishads

The process of becoming a self-caring person frequently involves self-healing our past. In order to move forward in our lives we may need to recall significant memories and reframe them as positive resources for our present and future. This is the crux of what most mental health therapy is about, but often the memories are not easily accessible while we are engaged in a discussion format. Memories of past traumas remain locked in our bodies while we struggle to reason our way to health. In order to make sense of the information gleaned from various health care experts, self-healing requires that we reconnect our bodies with our minds and learn various ways of working with our own mental dimension.

Forgotten Memories and Self-Healing

Our way of being in the world (the amount of tension we carry, what we expect from ourselves) is a natural response to events in our early lives. Sometimes in order to change unhealthy habits, we not only need to learn new ones and come to some understanding about the situations that stimulated our early responses. All of this can seem overwhelmingly complicated unless we begin to make the connection between then and now, and learn to think differently about the past.

The Case of the Lost Child Within

Meet Alice, a teacher of children in special education, who had a lot to learn from her own special child within. When Alice and I met she had already been to many doctors and experienced various types of physical therapies. She had tried medication, biofeedback, and just about anything else anyone suggested. Her problem, which had been going on for two years by that time, was a chronic pain in her right shoulder. Alice was referred to me by one of my former students who knew I did a kind of therapy that involved mental, emotional, and spiritual aspects of physical problems. On the intake sheet Alice had written, "You are my last hope."

I declined to occupy such a position of power over her future. I told her honestly that I did not know if I could help her but I was willing, if she was, to form a partnership to see what we could do together about the situation. I explained the work I would be doing with her, the Rubenfeld Synergy Method. We would begin by helping her to develop a fine-tuned awareness of her body. I would use gentle touch to focus and highlight her awareness. I would assist her to let go of extra habitual tension she might be carrying. If that tension was connected to any events in her life, past or present, we would deal with that aspect as well.

Slowly but steadily Alice and I discovered more about her physical self. Not surprisingly, her upper body, particularly her shoulders, was in a state of hypertension and unable to let go and relax. Her lower body (pelvis and legs) seemed to be too loose and lacking the strength to really support her.

Mentally Alice never stopped for a minute. She corrected students' papers in the waiting room before her sessions with me.

She made lists and outlines and planned what she was cooking for dinner. We discovered that the only time she took time out to relax was when her shoulder pain became severe. Then, in spite of her strong sense of duty, she delegated responsibility for dinner to her husband and children. Then, in pain, she allowed herself to sit in a recliner in her bedroom with a heating pad on her shoulder.

"One good thing this shoulder pain does for you is to give you some time to yourself to rest and recuperate," I said. "Do you think you could take care of yourself like that *without* your shoulder hurting?"

After a great deal of effort trying to imagine the situation I was proposing, Alice answered. "Maybe I could, but it would sure be a whole lot harder."

As months went by in our work together, Alice made small changes in the way she treated herself. She became more self-caring, allowing others to take over family chores, even when she wasn't in pain. This meant giving up the perfectionist way she *thought* things should be done. One day as I was working with her on releasing her shoulder she said, "It feels like there is a little fist inside that shoulder blade."

I asked her to make a fist with her hand and she noted that when she did that, the "little fist" inside her shoulder seemed to ease a bit. When Alice returned the following week, she reported a memory she had had while lying in bed. "I don't know if this has anything to do with anything, but I remembered that, as a child, I always pulled the covers up to my chin, and I'd sleep with my hands clutching the blanket." As she demonstrated the sleeping position, we both noted the raised position of her shoulders. This position was quite similar to the bracing posture she had walked around in habitually when we first met.

In the weeks that followed, the quality of our work together became more playful. Alice allowed herself to remember games and toys that she had loved as a child. It was during one of those playful, relaxing sessions that she suddenly looked up at me and said, matter-of-factly, "When I was growing up, my parents were both alcoholics. Could that have anything to do with all of this?"

As we continued our discussion, Alice remembered why she slept in that clutched position. She would go to bed, night after night, to the sound of her parents fighting. After she fell asleep, she would be awakened by their loud, aggressive voices. Remembering the situation that created the posture meant she reexperienced the feelings of fear and anger, but with the support of my presence. This enabled her to become more aware of the muscles involved in creating her tight shoulders. Beginning to release her chronically tight shoulders, she again reexperienced the feelings of fear and anger. Letting go of the feelings allowed her to further let go of the tension in her shoulders.

Elements of Self-Care

Many elements of self-care and self-healing are illustrated in Alice's story. She had "forgotten" her early childhood experiences, both pleasant and unpleasant. This left her in a state of constant physical and mental vigilance. Overdoing in her caretaking role, she had forgotten how to *play* or receive *support* from others. As she became more self-caring, she was able to *rest* without the excuse of pain. She was able to recall her past, reconnect with her inner child, and reframe her view of how she needed to be in the world now, as an adult. After she stopped bracing and continually getting ready for some unknown danger, she regained the ability to *rest*, receive *nourishment*, and enjoy *pleasure, laughter,* and *play.*

Using Our Minds

In recent years brain researchers have gained more clarity about the way that memories, experience, and learning are stored and retrieved in the body/mind. In order to develop confidence in the ability of one's mind to act on one's own behalf (to help us take care of ourselves), some understanding is needed of the complexity of such everyday experiences as remembering and forgetting.

According to Ernest Rossi, who reviewed hundreds of research articles on how the brain communicates with the body, all learning takes place in a particular body/mind state.[1] Most often, these states are not immediately accessible to what we call our "conscious mind." Sometimes these different states can be so separated from each other that they create separate personalities (as in the movie *The Three Faces of Eve*).

The Soma Twins and the Stress Response

I called on the Soma Twins to help us understand the way we can work with our mental dimension for self-healing and self-care.

Touchy began. "It shouldn't be too surprising that we lose some of our great ideas when you realize there are two times one hundred million possible mental states in each person's brain."

Feelie added, "One of the major difficulties for people in understanding and working with the mental dimension is the notion that all prior learnings are stored somewhere in their heads. Most people don't realize what Karl Pribram,[2] the brain researcher, discovered in his research. Mental images and content are not stored in little files in the brain but constructed each time they are accessed."

"And here's where we come in," Touchy said. "This reconstruction involves not only the brain but sensory and motor aspects of the body as well. We work closely with the hypothalamus, a special tissue about the size of a pea at the base of the forebrain."

Feelie joined in. "The hypothalamus receives the electrical impulses Touchy and I are sending from all parts of the nervous system. It integrates this information with the cognitive part of the mind (cerebral cortex) and then releases hormones to regulate a particular tissue of the body. Hormones are the messenger molecules that travel from the brain via the endocrine system (including the pituitary), altering the state of the body."

"Let's give a practical example," said Touchy. "Imagine you are on an airplane, reading, and the plane is in flight. You have a sensation of flutter in your stomach. You think 'Oops, this airplane just hit an air pocket.' Your hypothalamus sends a messenger molecule to the stomach, which first perceived the imbalance. This turns *off* the butterflies and other flutters of the body's alarm system."

"On the other hand," Touchy continued, "if the hypothalamus receives the following message from the mind: 'THIS IS IT!— Doomsday! The end of the world!' the messenger molecules traveling from your brain via the endocrine system (including the pituitary) will then alter the body state. The body responds: 'Turn on stress response.'"

Feelie explained, "So, the limbic-hypothalamic system of the brain is the central switching station. By receiving energy from one system (autonomic nerve, endocrine, or immune) and integrating it with mental processes (sensory, perceptual, emotional, and cognitive), this communication system plays an important part, not only in memory, but in learning, stress reduction, and healing."

I told the twins, "There are two things that stand out for me in what you are saying. In our culture we forget that there are other kinds of thought forms in the mind besides conscious analytical thought and the arrangement of logical sequences. The second part of this is that the body is capable of many kinds of thought forms connected to the five senses. Intelligence and memory are functioning even in the tiniest cell."

Feelie agreed, "The other kinds of thought forms include feeling states, sensory memories, focused imaginings, and kinetic memories. In fact, in order for these other forms to operate, we need to stop analyzing and commanding from the front brain."

"Anyone who has survived an important exam during schooling or professional training can attest to the fact that a certain level of relaxation and lessening of anxiety is necessary in order to make connections with what we know," said Touchy.

"The converse is also true—extreme anxiety and trauma can cause people to become amnesic about an event or period of their life. In fact, in order to recall a memory, it is often necessary to reenter or re-create the body/mind state which existed at the time of the initial learning or event," Feelie concluded.

The latest research shows that post-traumatic stress disorder (PTSD) develops in one out of three people who experience trauma. In America, an estimated 5 percent of people have PTSD at any given time. Symptoms of PTSD include anxiety, hallucinations, flashbacks, depression, loss of focus, nightmares, guilt, headaches, agitation, dizziness, panic attacks, chest pain, and insomnia. PTSD manifests in the limbic (responsible for fight or flight) part of the brain, thus leaving the survivor in an almost constant physical state of emergency.[3]

Muscle Memory

After my discussion with the twins, I remembered something dancers and athletes call "muscle memory." I guess now it could be more accurately called "whole-body memory." Here the person doesn't *think* about a tennis stroke or series of dance steps but goes back through the motions and the body remembers. The athletic coach says, "Practice the stroke the way I taught you until it gets in your body and you don't have to think about it."

As a choreographer's assistant, I had some unusual experiences with the part my body played in remembering. Choreographers create dances. They try out the steps and patterns on assistants who then teach the dance to other dancers. Choreographers seldom remember their own dances, especially if a lot of time has elapsed since they created them. After all, they don't repeatedly perform them. In our dance company, after a dance had been performed many times and then retired from the repertoire, I would be called upon to help reconstruct it. Even though I had performed the dance hundreds of times, I could recall very little of it consciously. But when the music was played and I began dancing the movements, my body began remembering one phrase after another.

This method would carry me only so far, and then I would draw a blank. I'd back up both the music and myself and "take it from the top," as we say in the theater. With each run-through, my body would re-member additional phrases, until a twenty-minute piece would finally be reconstructed. One particularly interesting thing about this method of recall: my body would remember the first version of the dance, not subsequent revisions or additions.

TEST YOUR MUSCLE MEMORY

1. Select an activity—a dance, game, or sport that you used to engage in but have not experienced for many years. It could be riding a bicycle or scooter, playing hopscotch, or dancing a polka. How about kick the can? or marbles? How long has it been since you climbed a tree?

2. In order not to alert your stress response, stay in a place of plea-sure, laughter, and play. The outcome of this experiment has no earth-shaking consequences—just the opportunity to explore your own "muscle memory" and learn to trust it.

3. As you perform the activity, take note of whether you simul-taneously remember people or other aspects of the situations

in which you engaged in the activity years ago. Consider this a bonus and reward for your willingness to put aside your adult "pride" and "dignity" in order to experience the clear sensory memories of *doing*.

Misuse of the Mind

Several years ago, as my colleagues and I moved into new office space, we found a poster left behind by the former tenants. Its title was "Seven Ways To Stagnate." We laughed at the familiarity of the items. There was nothing new on the list. We had heard all those reasons before. We just hadn't seen them all listed in the same place before:

> "It won't work."
> "It costs too much money."
> "We tried that last year."
> "It will take too long."
> "*They* won't like it!"
> "Nobody will come (or buy, or participate)."
> "It will take too much work and it's a dumb idea, anyway."

In working with clients, I am often reminded of this poster and its reference to misuse of the reasoning mind.

Cynthia was a nurse who had developed elaborate ways to stop herself from doing anything that was creative. And most of all, she stopped herself from looking forward to anything with enjoyment.

> "Whenever I start to feel good about something, like the conference I'm organizing for new nursing graduates, I start scaring myself by saying, 'What if . . .?' Then I come up with all the possible catastrophes I can imagine. I find myself picturing the most preposterous circumstances, like 'What if the lady who is bringing the refreshments has her baby two months early and isn't able to bring them?'"

I had another client who played what he called the "devil's advocate game." He'd think about doing something: taking a class, looking for another job, or asking a woman for a date. Then he would construct all the reasons why he *shouldn't* do any of those things. He was such an expert devil's advocate that he seldom ever attempted to do any of the things he initially thought of doing.

Affirming the Affirmative

In working with the mind, rather than concentrating on the glass being half empty, we need to elaborate on the picture of what a full glass would look like. Rather than living in fear that we might lose its contents, the work is to imagine how it might be if its gifts were overflowing.

I asked Cynthia to describe the conference she was preparing to present from the point of view of the *best* possible outcome. I introduced her to the idea of rehearsing for how she wanted things to turn out. Together we created an affirmation, a statement that encompassed her desires:

> *"I am preparing for the conference and enjoying the process of preparation."*

The first reaction she had to what seemed a kind of Pollyanna thinking was, "What if I can't get everything done that needs doing?"

"Are you the only person working on this project?"

"There are other people, but I have trouble trusting others to do what they say they will do."

We added a second affirmation to the first:

> *"I am acting with others to insure a successful conference, and I am developing confidence in myself and others to successfully carry out our responsibilities."*

ACTIONS FOR AFFIRMING

1. Select something that you want to accomplish and state it in the positive, as though it were already occurring. You might also write it down; studies have demonstrated that when we speak out loud and then write down affirmations in the positive, present tense, they are more effective.[4] Example:

   I am enjoying studying for my exam. I'm enjoying taking the exam from a place of comfort and confidence.

2. Listen carefully for any objections to be raised from your sensory awareness. You might experience a feeling of discomfort or hear a voice of objection: "What about . . ." (Watch out for the seven ways to stagnate.)

3. Resolve that objection by using the self-care skills:

   Sorting and Separating—"That was true when I was a child, but now, I am a grown person."

   Letting Go—Imagine the objections being surrounded by a cloud and floating up, up, and away.

   Using Partnership Power—"Together, I and (my friend, therapist, coach, Higher Power, spirit guide) can do this."

   Stepping Back—Allow yourself a panoramic perspective. See how things look from a satellite in outer space. How will the situation look 10 years from now?

   Exercising Choice—Give yourself permission to believe in the possibility of a positive outcome. As Bernie Siegel suggests, "When faced with uncertainty, there's nothing wrong with hope."[5]

The Everyday Trance

Self-care and self-healing require that the logical left brain quiet itself so that we may experience who we truly are and what our life is really about. One way that this occurs is in the everyday trance, which is a period of relaxation when the analytic mind is not in control. Nothing like the nightclub entertainer swinging his watch chain, trance states occur spontaneously every day. You drive your car on automatic pilot (a trance state) while thinking of what's for supper. You daydream (a trance state) during a pause in the proceedings at work. You suddenly notice that you have been singing to yourself for some time (auditory hallucination), or you experience a trance-forming feeling of calm as you walk softly on new snow or stand silently overlooking a breathtaking view of the valley below. When we don't have the time or the ability to relax in these ways, we begin to experience stress from the inside, and it becomes more difficult to move forward in living our external lives creatively.

From Critical to Creative

"I have been so critical of my husband lately, I really feel guilty," Doris told me on our first visit in six or seven years. "You were really helpful to me when I was considering marrying Steve, so I thought of you when I had a particularly bad week. I've thought my problem could be hormones or maybe allergies, but checking those out hasn't given me any real answers."

I encouraged Doris to continue to follow the recommendations of her other doctors, but I felt there were some things we could do together that might uncover what this hypercritical attitude was all about. Consciously, Doris knew that she was treating her husband like her father had treated her.

"I always hated that behavior, and I don't want to become like my father at this stage of my life."

Doris had taken leave from her job as a manager to complete a manuscript about working with handicapped children. She had been inspired to do this during a meditation retreat several years ago, but she was having trouble finishing the book. "Do you think your critical attitude has anything to do with the scary thing you have done in taking your leave?" I asked.

"Well, I don't feel very good about myself," Doris admitted, "since I'm not making the progress I intended to make by now. I have all kinds of plans and good ideas as I'm getting ready for bed, but the next morning is a different story. I keep getting distracted by errands I need to run or laundry that hasn't been done. This working from home isn't as easy as it looks."

As Doris began to deal with her feelings about herself, she recognized her disappointment in not living up to her own expectations. Then she discovered how critical and mean she was to herself. "I guess it's no wonder I'm critical of my husband," she said.

Since one of her main difficulties was taking action when she needed and wanted to accomplish something, I suggested she participate in a weekly movement group I was leading. (Through movement games and activities this group assists members in getting out of their critical minds and into a responsive body consciousness.) Doris was reticent at first, saying she didn't have a sense of rhythm, she always felt uncomfortable about her body, and she never could think of anything to do that was original. (More ways to stagnate!)

Changing Doris's mind about herself began as soon as she learned how to allow herself to go into a state of relaxation or everyday trance at the beginning of the group. At first she reported "falling asleep," but eventually she began to experience images as in a waking dream. The group helped her act out the image of herself standing in her kitchen, confused over what to do next, overreasoning to the point of paralysis.

Some members took the roles of her resistances, physically holding her back from the forward movement she was trying to accomplish. Other members shouted, "Come on, Doris, you can do it! Don't let them get you down! We're rooting for you!"

"It sounds crazy," Doris said, "but in the middle of that activity in the movement group, I realized that I'm afraid to act in any direction because I'll make a mistake. I'll be criticized. And if nobody else criticizes, the 'critical father' inside me will take over and do me in."

"Much of what you learned about yourself under the critical eyes of your father is not true," I told Doris. "You are learning in the group that you do have rhythm, and you can create original actions as long as you don't *think* too hard about it."

Therapeutic Trance

As Doris discovered, information, in trance states, may be generated or recalled with ease. Healing occurs when the re-creation of the memory can be done with some significant difference from the original event. Positive feelings are present as well as negative ones. Rather than experiencing the isolation of the original negative situation, you are in the presence of at least one other person, or you are working with a tool for transforming the situation to produce a different outcome. Doris achieved a breakthrough by reenacting a difficult situation in the movement group. You can try this method of bypassing your critical self by following the directions in "Movements for Mending" in appendix A. Other ways to access your creative self are to use drawing or some other art technique that accesses the imagery side of the brain. (See movement VIII in appendix A.)

The Power of an Image

According to Jeanne Achterberg,[6] a powerful source of our creativity is the mind's ability to image. Imagery, more than just creating pictures, is the thought process that invokes and uses the senses. Whether seeing or smelling, hearing or tasting, touching or sensing movement and position in space, these are all ways that the body/mind communicates with itself. In this two-way street, our bodies are affected by images that we hold, and the wisdom of our bodies can generate images. We can construct new images or call to mind images we need to remember for our own healing.

Healing a Self-Image

Meet Peggy, a social work administrator who at age 40 was finally learning what it meant to take care of herself. On a disability leave from her job at the State School for the Developmentally Disabled when I first met her, Peggy had a long history of doing a good job for her clients and the people she supervised—and taking very poor care of herself. She had stopped her alcohol abuse, but she had transferred her dependency to an old habit of abusing herself with food.

After a few months of our work together and a few weeks of AA meetings, Peggy said, "I didn't know what 'self-care' or 'taking care of myself' meant. I thought taking care of myself was goofing off or doing what I wanted to do. It never occurred to me that taking care of myself might be paying my bills, or cleaning my house, or refraining from eating unhealthy foods."

"Many people share your misconception. That's why it is necessary to do some self-healing in order to start becoming self-caring," I said.

"I've always had such a bad self-image," Peggy said with a look of disgust on her face. "I'm not sure where it all comes from—the abuse I got as a kid from my older cousin or the fact that I was fat when I was little. I've always felt inadequate—like I just wasn't enough."

I asked Peggy if she was willing to consider a different opinion of herself. She looked surprised that this was something she could change. I said, "Sometimes, before you meet someone personally, you may have a negative opinion of the person based on what others have told you or how the person looks or dresses. Once you get to know the person for yourself, you change your mind. So, how well do you know yourself to have formed such a strong negative opinion?"

She smiled. "Well, of course I don't know myself well at all. I've been spending my energy following rabbit trails that don't even lead to the rabbit."

I suggested we experiment with a way to access another part of her brain using a tool that I have always called Barry's Bodywork. I first learned it from Barry Stevens, one of my teachers.[7] I told her to close her eyes, go inside, and tell me where her awareness goes. She pointed to her solar plexus, and I asked her to describe what she found there.

"It feels warm," she said, "and I see something red, like a flame, a glowing flame." Surprised by how easily the images came, Peggy opened her eyes and said with some delight, "Hey, this is OK!"

I asked that she go back inside and become an observer of whatever happens and report to me what she notices. "Let's try an experiment," I said. "I'd like you to say, '*I'm* OK!' and notice what happens inside."

Peggy complied with my suggestion and then, she said, "The warm sensation is still there, but it's increasing, as though the flame is burning fuller. She paused to reflect on what was happening inside. "Now I feel full. You know, it's like that feeling of satisfaction you have after a good meal."

"Let's try another sentence," I suggested. "Try saying, 'I am enough.'"

Peggy again repeated the sentence I had given her. "Wow! Now the warm sensation is really strong. She repeated, "I am enough," and then the other side of her brain got it. "I *am* enough!" she said with delight.

Meditation

The original *Stillpoint* was quite comprehensive in relation to somatic methods for caregivers to take care of themselves. But one important method was not mentioned—meditation. Various forms of meditation are ancient, but Western approaches at the time often involved a focus on a denial of the body, or a way to overcome the body. Fortunately, much has changed and now we have forms to recommend that we would consider embodied.

Jamie McHugh approaches meditation from his perspective as a dancer and nature photographer. His Embodied Mindfulness follows Zen master Shunryu Suzuki's suggestion that *"to stop your mind does not mean to stop the activities of the mind. It means your mind pervades your whole body."*[8] In Jamie's words, "Embodied Mindfulness practices can be viewed as simply a way to grow the brain map of your body by refining your inner sensing and your fine motor movement in a relaxed, easy state of awareness."[9]

AUTHOR REFLECTIONS

Sheila: In the fall of 1995, as I was racing out the door to the airport, I took one more look around. I noticed a package from the Institute of Noetic Sciences in the pile of mail on the dining room table. It was a book the organization had sent me as a bonus for joining. "Might be good to have something to read while I'm in the hospital with Rose," I thought, so I stuck it in my carry-on. The book turned out to be a manual for staying in the present moment. *Wherever You Go, There You Are* accompanied me as I accompanied Rose through each of the 14 days of her dying. It helped to hold us both in an exquisite journey of what author Jon Kabat-Zinn calls "moment-to-moment awareness,"[10] or mindfulness. 🌸

Christine: Like Sheila, I have always found movement to be a way for me to move into a meditative state. For years I avoided meditation because even the thought of sitting still was too much. Being a kinesthetic being, I have learned over the years that if I stretch, walk, or exercise before I sit to meditate I can settle my mind. My favorite is when I combine meditation with movement. Walking the labyrinth is personally my most effective and satisfying form of mediation. 🌸

Reframing

Our mental attitude either contributes to or takes away from the spirit of what is happening in our world—like the frame around a picture. A powerful tool for self-care and self-healing is to change the way we view a particular incident or situation—to reframe it.

I remember a reframing experience that happened for me when the health center where I had recently started to work opened two new employee parking lots. This practical convenience soon became the object of much consternation as different individuals and groups began vying for particular spots in the lot nearer the staff entrance. I found myself getting caught up in the issues as others saw it until I stepped back and took a broader view.

The urban university I had recently attended had 25,000 students and 9,000 parking places, a dismal situation indeed. Looking at the present situation from the perspective (frame of reference) of my prior experience, I came to feel a parking place within a block or two would be a joyous privilege, and the brief walk a welcome price to pay!

The Humor Frame

Humor is an effective tool that can be helpful in reframing a situation. It can allow us to change our perspective from negative to positive, from life-or-death serious to not-so-important after all. When we learn how to use humor to reframe, we are better able to maintain balance and sanity in our work and family life.

The scenario of each person's ongoing, ever-unfolding life experience can be seen as a personal situation comedy or a tragic soap opera. We don't need high-paid scriptwriters to invent situations because, from moment to moment, we have the opportunity to create a soap opera or a situation comedy out of what is happening in our real lives. Let's try some role-playing.

REFRAMING WITH HUMOR: AN EXERCISE

SCENARIO—(SOAP OPERA)

Take a situation in which you have felt aggravated. Remember when you found yourself getting in an uproar over some familiar or unfamiliar aggravation, inconvenience, insult, or injury (real or imaginary). Reliving that moment, now imagine someone asks you, "What's the matter?"

Pause! Breathe! Imagine a channel-switching remote control in your left hand. Click! Decide! On which channel do you want to play this particular scenario? Would this be a good soap opera?

Scene: "Transforming Your Aggravation"—Take #1

Decide which character you want to play and begin feeding lines to those persons (characters) standing nearby. See if they are able to improvise their lines based on what you are saying to them. If the lines the characters are speaking seem appropriate to the soap opera, and if you find playing this role a satisfying way to live, see how far you can take this.

Consider renting a video camera and crew. You might make a demonstration tape (called demo in the industry). See if you can sell this act as a pilot to one of the major networks. Should you get turned down, consider independent syndication. If all else fails, make believe you are involved in afternoon reruns of your soap opera, and this will give you the opportunity to repeat this particular scenario in this particular manner on a daily basis.

SCENARIO—(SITUATION COMEDY)

Scene: Transforming Your Aggravation—Take #2

Remember that situation in which you were in an uproar, as above. Imagine someone asks you, "What is the matter?"

Pause! Breathe! Ask yourself, "How would this matter play as a situation comedy?" Select a comic character you feel would do the greatest justice to your situation, and play the scene from that vantage point. You can call on inner guides in the guise of famous comedians you have known. How would Lucille Ball play this part? How about Chris Rock? Traditionalists might prefer Charlie Chaplin. (Practice his walk now.) How might Sarah Silverman play this scene? Or Jerry Seinfeld?

Should you develop self-discipline enough in your real-life situations to choose the situation-comedy-routine option more than several times in the same week (especially when the matter is the same old matter), you will begin to discover that the Joker in the Sky (or whoever is in charge of humor energies) will never let you run out of humorous variations on any of your life's themes.

AUTHOR REFLECTIONS

Sheila: In the years between the first edition of *Stillpoint* and this second one, exploring more how the mental dimension affects our lives has proved invaluable. The notion of mindset from the theory of resilience has caused me to remind myself often, "It matters what we say to ourselves." If we say we will never recover from something, we probably won't.

My understanding of how muscle memory works and the conditions necessary to heal an earlier traumatic experience have deepened. A scene from teaching Interplay at a Women's prison comes to mind.

The game we were playing is sometimes called the "magic spot," in which we establish a theme (this time it was "rain") and a member of the group starts us off by doing a repetitive movement we all copy. The group movement continues until someone steps onto the "magic spot." Everyone stops. The person on the spot says three sentences inspired by the word and then becomes the new leader, introducing a new repetitive movement we all follow. After several women took turns describing incidents of being "caught in the rain" or liking to "sit inside by a fireplace when it's raining," a woman took her turn describing the fun of stomping in a rain puddle, enjoying the splashing. She then said in a distraught voice, "The worse beating I ever got was when I was five years old and I soiled my new Easter Sunday clothes playing in a rain puddle before church." She then broke down remembering the pain.

The whole group clustered around the woman, eventually giving her a group hug, and she began recovering from reliving the memory. Observing the scene I realized that she would always have that negative memory, but now, alongside it forever would be this positive memory of the loving support of her community. ✿

Christine: When I think about the mental aspects of self-care, I think about two things: self-compassion and affirmations. I recently had a conversation with my friend and colleague, Dr. Cynthia Phelps, owner of Inner Allies and a Mindful Self-Compassion Trainer through Kristen Neff's program. I asked her, "How does self-compassion relate to self-care and self-healing?" Cynthia replied, "Self-compassion is the ability to recognize that you are suffering and to, then, be kind and supportive of yourself. This starts with observing your internal self-talk and noticing if it is harsh and critical and, if so, shifting it to be more forgiving and kind. From here, you can take physical actions to be compassionate to yourself (self-care), such as giving yourself a rest, treating your body with kindness (moving, exercising, getting a massage), or eating some healthy food." She went on to say, "Caregivers of all types are at risk for burnout and compassion fatigue. Burnout is characterized by feelings of overwhelming exhaustion, depression, depersonalization, cynicism, loss of meaning in work, and a sense of inefficacy. Burnout consequences are both emotional and physical and result in poor self-care, and can be a threat to the caregiver's own safety as well as to the safety of those they are serving." Just in physicians alone, the frequency of burnout was found to be 41 percent in a 2011 study of 7000 physicians. By 2014, burnout rates increased in all specialties and in late 2015, a Mayo Clinic study found that more than half of American physicians have at least one sign of burnout.[11]

As to affirmations—my clients will tell you I am a huge believer in affirmations, stating things in the positive and writing them down! I have been personally practicing this for years. I call these manifesting moments. I take time to sit quietly and really get present with myself and what I am wanting to change or create. I then write it down as though it has already become a reality and read it out loud to myself. If it is a habit I am trying to change or focus on, I might write it and tape it to my bathroom mirror so it stays in the forefront of my consciousness. Sometimes I use the words in an art piece in order to play with what I am trying to create. I find it helps to do this work after a yoga session, a walk, or a dance class so that my mind is able to settle down and listen. ❀

SUMMARY

In living a self-caring lifestyle we are affected by habits of the past, beliefs we have about ourselves and about how others view us, and the feelings and attitudes we bring to the helping situation. The dance of self-care in the mental dimension involves

Focusing on difficulties, barriers, and problems ———
your body responds to this negative picture ———
leading to your constructing even more negative consequences
resulting in your becoming ———DRAINED.

OR

Imagining a desired state ———
your body /mind system responds, giving you
opportunity to deal with objections raised from any part of you
leading to elaboration of the goal and confidence in a positive
outcome resulting in your becoming ———
ENERGIZED.

AND

Living in a critical, analyzing frame of mind ———
creates tension in the body ———
leading to mental stagnation and lack of creativity ———
resulting in becoming ———DRAINED.

OR

Living close to your imagining mind ———
allows relaxation in the body ———
leading to creative reframing, healing laughter, and solutions
resulting in becoming ———ENERGIZED.

Get up offa dat thing.
Dance an you'll feel bettah.
–James Brown

8
Remodeling and Reframing: The Emotional

What I am feeling and how I feel about it are the essence of my experience, and as such are also the essence of both my development and my degeneration.

–Deane Juhan, *Job's Body*[1]

I saw an amazing picture of a heart cell on television. Sitting in a dish by itself, the heart cell was pulsing visibly to its own internal rhythm. The camera panned back to show another heart cell in another dish nearby, also pulsing with its own rhythm. Their rhythms were quite different until they were placed in the same dish. Even before they touched, their pulsations synchronized into one continuous shared beat. I remember thinking, "It's no wonder feelings are so contagious; our whole biological system is programmed to synchronize." Just being in the same room with somebody who is depressed or frightened or lethargic can mean those same states of feeling are evoked in us. That being the bad news, the good news of our vulnerability is that laughter, joy, and courage are contagious too.

Feelings are the stuff of our kinesthetic senses. They are physical sensations not connected with sight, hearing, taste, or smell. Feelings are subjective perceptions of our own body sensations, and when a feeling is intensified it becomes an emotion. There are as many words to describe feeling states as there are words for the flavors of ice cream, but most are variations of a central few. As people who do caring work, we must be able to connect with others at a feeling level without becoming emotionally drained ourselves. We must be able to identify and express our own feelings and to allow others to express theirs. Avoiding feelings drains our energy, and being around somebody who avoids his or her feelings can be draining as well.

In the interest of our own self-caring, we need to be clear about our own feeling states and learn how not to take on other people's feelings. If, after we spend time together, the other person (client, student, child, spouse, or friend) feels better and we feel worse, the situation has not improved at all. The score just went from lose-win to win-lose, and only win-win counts.

Errors in the Emotional Dimension

There are two common errors in relation to feelings: not knowing what you are feeling, and using one feeling to avoid another. Not knowing what we are feeling may come from years spent in higher education. There, intellectual processes are believed to operate without the information feelings provide. But feelings are essential guides for living. Our lives need to flow from our feeling values, and our feelings tell us what we care deeply about. One psychologist I know described himself as "monolithic about feelings"; any sensation he experienced turned quickly into a mild-to-severe irritation, which came across as anger. A lady whose children had been taken away from her through the trickery of her husband reported that she had been crying nonstop for days; I asked if she ever allowed herself to get angry and suggested it might be time to get mad. These two examples show how, when one feeling is used to avoid others, the substitute feeling becomes extreme.

From Anxiety to Excitement

Mark was a young graduate student who had been participating in a movement group I was leading on his college campus. The men in the group had explored different kinds of movement including yoga, dance, tai chi, and systems of self-defense. Emerging from these explorations was a realization of their overreliance on logic and analytical skills while ignoring or avoiding feelings. Mark had been struggling for several months, trying to come up with a topic for his dissertation in psychology. People had warned him that, since he would live with this decision for a long time, he needed to be certain to make the right choice for himself, now and for his future. One morning he reported the following breakthrough to the group:

"I was in the library looking through materials, trying to come up with a topic for a paper I had to write. I noticed that when I came across material on a particular subject I got a fluttery sensation in my stomach. When I put the material aside, the sensation left. Later, I came across something else related to the same topic, and the sensation returned. All of a sudden it hit me. Instead of my usual anxiety, I was feeling mildly excited about that subject. Then I thought, 'Maybe this could be a way to select my dissertation topic!' I've concluded that if I start out with a subject I have some excitement about, it will be easier to keep motivated for the long haul."

Other Feeling Errors

Feelings are contagious, and sometimes experiencing an emotion at an extreme level means that you have taken on someone else's feelings. A teenage girl whose family had recently endured a "polite" divorce told me she felt angry a great deal of the time. In addition to helping her express her anger appropriately, I worked with the more placid members of the family on allowing their anger. This way she didn't have to be angry for everyone else.

Self-healing requires that we each be able to experience a full range of emotions, because healing takes place through the full experience of the appropriate feelings. Feelings that have been driven too deeply within (stuffed) keep us from maturing into our real selves. Let's meet a man who came to me asking to get his body back. At first he reported feeling numb from the neck down and unable to identify or experience any feelings except vague discomfort.

Good Grief

I almost didn't recognize Jake in the crowded clinic waiting room. He seemed taller and more vibrant than when I had last seen him a year ago. Jake had been in his late 30s when we started working together several years ago, but somehow he looked younger now than when we first met. Jake had requested this appointment for what he called an "emotional check-in." He flashed a familiar broad smile as he extended his hand and enthusiastically shook mine.

"There are some things you didn't tell me about getting my body back," Jake said as soon as the door to my office shut behind us.

"I wasn't aware of keeping anything from you. What have you discovered?"

"I've been having the strangest experiences lately, and I don't really know what to make of them. Maureen and I finally broke it off for good six months ago, and I'm doing really well. I've been able to see her kids and keep my relationships with them going strong. And when Maureen and I see each other, it's surprisingly pleasant."

I was remembering the painful sessions with Maureen and Jake as she attacked and he hid, frozen with fear and guilt. We worked to make the relationship more rewarding for both of them, and then finally the focus was on finding a way to end it. "All the hard work you have done is paying off," I suggested. "You weren't able to put the relationship together, but it sounds as though you have found a way to release each other from cycles of blaming and feeling guilty."

"If anyone had told me three years ago that I would be able to feel this clear of Maureen, I would never have believed it," Jake said, while gesturing with his hand up and down in front of his chest.

"You can take lots of credit for the work you have done to make this clarity possible," I said.

Jake smiled and said, "I remember when I first came to you, I couldn't cry. I would get angry or depressed, or what I called 'frustrated.' But that was just my way of getting ready to work myself up into being angry."

"And the two of you were quite a pair," I reminded him. "Maureen didn't know how to cry, either. She blamed you for not being in touch with your feelings and for somehow being responsible for her unhappiness. You would take in her bad feelings and carry them around for weeks."

"I remember the day Maureen and I had a joint appointment with you after you and I had done a bodywork session. I was able to express my pain to Maureen about the relationship not working."

I, too, was remembering that day as Jake described it. "After you allowed yourself to cry in the individual session, you and Maureen were both able to experience and express your grief to each other. That was the beginning of your individual and collective healing."

Jake nodded in agreement. "But that is what's so confusing now," he said. "I went to a concert the other evening with some friends at that church on Elm Street. I was feeling at peace with myself and with my life. The environment and the music were exquisite. I felt inspired by the whole experience until I noticed my eyes welling up with tears. I wiped my eyes, looked around carefully to see if anyone saw me, and then settled back into my seat. Before long it was happening again. You didn't tell me that when I learned how to cry I wouldn't be able to shut the tears off. And in public, too!" Jake said, half teasingly.

"You were touched by the music and the beauty of your surroundings. Tears aren't just for expressing grief and sadness. Whenever something important happens, tears well up. It's your body's way of saying, "Pay attention. This really matters.""

A FEELING QUIZ

Test your Emotional I.Q. with the following quiz. Cover all of the columns in the chart below except column one titled "feeling." Now look down the list and ask yourself the following:

Which feeling(s) do you allow yourself to feel?

Which feeling(s) is missing from your vocabulary?

Which feeling do you have a tendency to get stuck in?

Which feeling do you have trouble allowing someone else to express without taking it on?

Uncover the other headings in the chart below. Describe your own subjective experience of each of the feelings listed. Next, note the suggestions of things to do and the description of some of the physical changes that may be occurring in your body.

FEELING	SUBJECTIVE EXPERIENCE	PHYSICAL CHANGES	THINGS TO DO
FEAR	rigid, shallow breath, inner chills	parasympathetic nervous system activated	keep moving, get support, express unexpressed feeling
ANGER	tight chest, increased energy, stomach discomfort	stress chemicals activated	take assertive action, reframe as not serious, make creative expression
ANXIETY	shortness of breath, sweaty palms, muscle tension	lactic acid produced as waste product	change breathing, reframe as not serious, laugh
JOY	warm sensations, internal massage	increased oxygen to blood, tension relieved	make creative expression, hug someone
DEPRESSION	lump in throat, labored breathing	endocrine and immune system suppressed	grieve, make creative expresion

Ecstasy: A Special Emotion

One reason to take special care of ourselves is that there are some positive experiences in life for which we will need our energy—one such experience is ecstasy. We believe ecstasy, not often on the list of usual emotions, is a part of our birthright as human beings. Not exclusively erotic, ecstasy is a powerful emotion of rapturous delight. Each generation of young children seems to discover anew the ancient secrets known to the whirling dervishes and Sufi dancers. Do you remember, as a young child, laughing and giggling, turning and turning until you fell down, and then getting up to do it again? Or perhaps you remember rolling down a hill in the soft grass, discovering a path to altering your consciousness and discovering ecstasy.

Ecstasy is achieved by . . .
approaching slowly from
a place of stillness
when you have committed
yourself to an exploration
of total openness to your
own and to another's ebb
and flow.
Allowing alternating rhythms,
you move towards synchronizing,
with all parts of yourself as
well as with the universe.
Containment is necessary in order
to allow excitement to build,
until the ecstatic movement,
the moment of truth,
when we are able to allow
total surrender!
Each time is the first time,
for we are born again
with each complete and
total act of surrender!

Balance in Caring and Self-Care

We caregivers are sensitive to other people's feelings. Though helpful at times, this sensitivity can be a problem and a serious barrier to our own self-care. Meet Sally, a nurse manager in her mid-40s who wanted to learn to set limits with a grown son and to be supportive to her mother, who was ill with cancer. As the "mother in the middle" Sally was often pulled in opposite directions, having trouble taking care of herself in the midst of competing demands.

Lessons of the Mother Bird

"I'm close to exhaustion," Sally said. "The responsibility with mother's illness has been overwhelming these past nine months. And here I am, trying to finish my degree while working full-time and dealing with a 24-year-old son who lies around the house all day."

Sally breathed a huge sigh of relief as she spoke, unloading some of the concerns she had been carrying around for the past months. As an only child she has been a wonderful daughter to her mother, and interactions related to her mother's illness had brought them even closer.

"You have been helping your mother to die, and now it looks as though she is going to live longer than anyone expected," I said, after getting more background on the subject.

"I guess that's a big part of it," Sally said, concluding with another labored sigh. "Right now, though, I feel more concerned about my relationship with my son. I just had a fight with him, and I feel horrible. He hasn't worked in seven or eight months, and I feel I'm not helping him by allowing him to live there without looking for a job."

Over the weeks and months of our work together, Sally was able to discover how she took on other people's feelings. As we worked to heighten her kinesthetic senses, she noted the tension she created in her body when dealing with the feelings of her family members. When her mother was depressed about her illness, Sally felt tension around her heart and worried that she might have caused her mother to feel that way. After all, she had been wondering to herself how long she could sustain the caretaker role. When her son was angry with her, Sally felt tight in her shoulders and stomach. She asked herself what she had done to contribute to his anger. After all, she had been involved with work and school and her mother; maybe he needed more time with her.

Sally told me later that the turning point for her came after an image of a mother bird had come to her during one of our sessions together. While she was in a state of relaxation, I asked her what advice the mother bird would give to her if it could talk to her in English.

"I see the mother bird in the spring, getting food for her young. She chews it, even partially digesting it, before giving it to her chicks. By summer the mother bird teaches the chicks to fend for themselves, pushing them out of the nest to fly on their own. Her message, "There are many phases to nurturing and various styles to the different seasons of our caring."

It took lots of practice, but Sally was able to stop taking on other people's feelings and to consider her own feelings in her relationships with her family.

"I felt very invigorated when I finally realized I could still feel good about myself, even when my son was acting like a jerk!" Sally said proudly. And since I am not in charge of my mother's happiness any longer, I think she appreciates the freedom to have a down day or two without my taking it on and trying to fix it."

Healthy Anger

Anger can be a constructive emotion, but in my family nobody knew that. People expressed what we called anger: arguing, swearing, screaming—I still remember the screaming. I used to think this meant we had permission to be angry until I realized that our expressions of anger were followed by guilt and shame. I now understand that we had confused anger with rage. What we were expressing was rage that is old, previously shamed anger. We weren't able to deal with the immediate situation that called for anger because of old, unresolved issues that had become rage. When people stuff their anger this often leads to rage later. When anger is respected and honored, important issues can be dealt with. Anger is a healthy emotion and, as with most other feelings,

Avoiding anger makes you sick.

Repressing anger makes you sick.

Expressing anger when you aren't honoring it leads to shame and guilt, which makes you sick.

Denying anger makes you sick.

Holding on to anger as resentment makes you sick.

Confusing rage with anger leads to lack of control, which leads to discounting of your anger (more shame and guilt), which makes you sick.

AN ODE TO ANGER
by Sheila K Collins

Anger is my truth, my life's spark.
Anger is my firepower.
Anger is the power to be, to become,
to make happen, to resolve.
Anger is my connection to the
electric universe.

Storms clear the air,
cleaning smog and cobwebs
out of the atmosphere.
Light follows thunder, revealing
clarity in the stark edges of the
moist dawn.

How would our lives be different if we could greet each other's anger as a life spark, a powerful connection to the electric universe? Learning to honor our own and other people's anger is not easy. Perhaps we should form the "Society for the Expression of Healthy Anger." We could practice expressing anger without hurting ourselves or others. We would need to be careful not to take ourselves too seriously, since anger does not have to be grim or ugly. Some suggested movements for society members to practice might include the following:

Stomping—Flamenco dancers do it while clapping their hands and shaking their castanets. People in the north woods do it to keep warm, to get the snow off their boots, to celebrate their connections to the earth. Stomping is a way to define boundaries, to clarify meaning.

Growling—Animals do it, like puppies at play. Sometimes we play too rough. It's a way to let the other person know, "You're going too far. Back off. Don't take me for granted."

Spitting—Young boys do it, after much practice, in contests with one another. It is useful for underlining and punctuating important points in your argument. Women, due to cultural constrictions, suffer from spit deprivation and may need to practice privately until they develop the skill to meet their intended mark. Fair-fighting rules demand that spitting not be a body-contact sport. One must not aim for an individual, and avoid doing it into the wind.

Chewing—People usually do it with food, tobacco, or gum. Domestic animals prefer bones, leather, and rubber balls. Since we are dealing with the most flexible joint in the body (the jaw), care must be taken that these movements not result in self-harm. After chewing on your anger issues for some time, it is important to move to other, more expressive methods to release the anger energy and save your teeth, TMJ joints, and jaw, face, and neck muscles.

Punching—Cowboys, James Bond, and other cultural heroes do it on TV. Since nobody really gets hurt, these performances mislead people into thinking that this is not a potentially damaging and lethal activity. The truth is, punching is for punching bags and for pillows, sometimes while one is wearing protective gloves.

Singing in the Shower—I've found the shower stall the best place to try out any of the above activities. I especially love singing in the small, enclosed chamber. The privacy eliminates any self-consciousness, and the reverberations support and magnify the sound of this ex-formational activity.

Complacency

Christine: I started thinking about complacency during a poetry workshop led by John Fox,[2] the founder of the Institute of Poetic Medicine. He asked us to write an ode to an emotion, which led me to think about my white privilege and the ways it had worked in my life—including my sense of self-satisfaction in places where I was unaware of the bigger picture and how my ignorance contributed to it. When we are complacent as individuals, it can lead to danger for ourselves and others. It could be a detriment to our health as we stay in jobs that are toxic for us or our families. Furthermore, it could be dangerous for the greater society if we witness atrocities and don't speak up for those who are marginalized and oppressed, creating dis-ease in the larger whole body of our world. ❋

AN ODE TO COMPLACENCY
by Christine Gautreaux

There you are.
My old dear friend . . .
My frayed and washed-out sweater
I continue to wrap around my shoulders
when you no longer fit.
You have kept me sheltered
and warm
in my privileged bubble
while others have gone cold and hungry,

naked in this unjust world.
It is time to set you down,
pass you on,
or better yet
unravel you back to your truest form
and re-knit a new reality.
One that includes all races,
all genders, all faiths.
Each of us, everyone,
stitched together with
peace, love, and safety.

How would it change your world if you honestly looked at the areas in your life where you've become complacent? It could be your self-care, your health, a job you hate, or relationships that have been detrimental to you. Change can be a challenge, but what would you do if you knew you could not fail? We could practice unraveling our complacency by playing with the following:

Shape & Stillness: Using your whole body or just one hand, create a shape and hold it for longer than feels comfortable. Then quickly change to a new shape. Hold that shape for longer than feels comfortable and slowly change to a new shape. Play around with holding different shapes that want to come out of your body for different periods of time and vary the way you transition to new shapes. Take a moment to savor the effect you have created for yourself.[3]

Lie Down: Go from standing in the middle of your living space to lying down on the floor. How did your perspective change? What do you see from this angle?

Shake: Indigenous cultures teach us the importance of shaking in their dances and rituals. We can shake things out of our bodies that are stressful and no longer needed or we can just "shake things up!" Put on a piece of music approximately five minutes long, and shake different parts of your body and then your whole body. See what you notice.

The Soma Twins On Emotions

I checked in with Touchy and Feelie about feelings and got their suggestions on dealing with our emotional dimension.

Feelie volunteered first. "Most people spend way too much time avoiding feelings or holding on too long to a feeling that, though unpleasant, is familiar. And when there is a continual repetition of the same feeling, other feelings are usually being avoided."

"Some avoidance of feelings comes from the fact that families and cultures have lists of approved and forbidden feelings," Feelie added. "Some families do not allow expressions of anger, while others allow little else. In some countries like the United States, men are discouraged from crying, and grieving is considered a private matter. In other countries, grief and mourning are expressed publicly in elaborate rituals. Men and women flagellate themselves and march through the streets to the sound of a funeral dirge."

"As far as the body/mind is concerned," Touchy says, "feelings are transient signals and expressions of inner needs and values. Tears often accompany one's letting go emotionally and physically. Feelings also provide information about what is happening in the environment and what direction to take."

Feelie adds, "It is possible to pick up the feelings of someone else, especially if that person is not in touch with his or her own feelings. The key to self-care here is to note the information you are getting from your own visceral sensations. If your stomach is grinding and you can't identify anything that is happening with you, ask the person you are with to check inside her- or himself. If the signal belongs to the other person, let it go on through you."

"There is a vicious cycle that becomes activated when we hold on to or avoid certain feelings," Touchy continued. "Anger activates stress hormones, and it increases adrenaline and other chemical secretions harmful to our bodies, especially if continued over a long period of time. People can become 'hot reactors,' as Paul Pearsall describes in his book *Super Immunity*.[4] When activated repeatedly, this heightened state produced by adrenaline can become as addictive as any other psychoactive drug."

Feelie agreed and added, "People don't have to drink to get high. They can get high from their own brain chemicals generated by rage. Women in our culture are more likely to get hooked in a vicious cycle related to depression, becoming what Pearsall calls 'cool reactors.' If a life situation leads to a feeling of helplessness, biochemical changes take place in the brain. Norepinephrine, which is produced in the central nervous system, is depleted. This accentuates feelings of depression, which further deplete norepinephrine, which—you guessed it—leads to more feelings of depression. And all of this affects the immune system and the type of diseases people are likely to incur."

"What needs to happen," said Touchy, "is to interrupt (or reverse) the cycle. Physical movement (exercise, dance, yoga) increases the production of chemicals that contribute to a sense of well-being. People can contribute to their own self-care by participating in activities to reverse the downward spiral of negative emotions."

"One problem," Feelie said, "is that people tend to think of feelings as pleasant or unpleasant, pleasurable or painful. This doesn't work too well, because then people try to hold on to or recapture pleasurable feelings and avoid what they are afraid will be painful feelings. A better way to think of feelings is whether they are of the productive or dead-end type."

"Holding on to any feeling," said Touchy, "will become dead-end because the system has to shut down to some extent. But the negative emotions pose special difficulties. Fear, panic, guilt, shame, and repressed anger all activate the stress system and inhibit the immune system. Laughter and the positive emotions boost the immune system, increase circulation, and provide an internal massage to the heart, lungs, and stomach!" Both of the twins looked triumphant as they delivered the message, "It is better for our bodies, minds, and spirits to cultivate the positive emotions and to learn to interrupt the vicious cycles of negative emotions. We do this by taking care of the business of our life that has attracted or created them, and then moving the negative emotions through and out into the universe."

"Developing a strong sense of humor," said Feelie, "may be the most pivotal element in self-care and self-healing, particularly for the folks who do the work of caring for others."

Lightening Up with Humor

Since feelings are the stuff of our experience, taking responsibility for our feelings means taking responsibility for our life. Just as a glass can be seen as half empty or half full, we have a choice: to focus on the dark or the light, the disheartening or the enlivening aspects of our experience. Humor is a vehicle that gives us that choice. We can choose humor not just to cheer ourselves up or to deny our experience of difficulties but to bring about a balance for our self-care and self-healing. Developing a sense of humor gives us the choice of looking at things from a lighter side. Humor disarms aspects of a situation (or of ourselves) that may have taken on more importance than they deserve. Even if you think you don't have a sense of humor, you can develop one.

- Do you forget the punch line when you try to tell a joke?
- Were you noted in your high school yearbook as a "serious thinker"?
- Did you learn firsthand the hard lesson that it isn't fun to be the butt of a prankster's ridicule?

Do not despair, at least not until you have read further and learned how to perform comedic tragedy. One thing to keep in mind as you attempt to break the shackles of your humorless past: you have a great advantage working for you. Since no one, perhaps not even you, expects you to deliver a humorous response, your next joke has been set up by your usual serious facade. I remember the response my dad, a quiet, serious man, used to get from friends and neighbors whenever he would say something funny. His most powerful ally, the punch to his punch line, was the element of surprise.

RX FOR HUMOR BUILDING

Now for actions on your own behalf. Just as you can change your diet and eating habits, you can begin to develop a humor habit. Laughter and play can feed your spirit as well as your immune and endocrine systems. If you have decided to make humor a key part of your self-care/self-healing plans, here are some actions to take:

Exaggerate! Almost anything becomes ludicrous if you do it big enough or dramatically enough or fast enough. What is your tendency? Are you serious? Determined? Scattered? Do it more.

- Place the back of your hand on your forehead and rise to your full height, head tilted slightly backwards, face to the sky. Picture yourself as a damsel in distress, the star of your own melodrama. (If you weigh 250 pounds and wrestle for a hobby, this will work even better.)
- Old-time silent movies seem funny partly because they are

speeded up, causing the movements to be jerky. Enliven monotonous, dreary tasks by performing them in old-time-movie style, just for the fun of it.

Speak without words, using sounds or nonsense syllables. In InterPlay we call this your own made-up language. It carries the emotional load without the reality-show details.

Imagine a different reality. Picture horns or wings on the people you must be around in a difficult situation. At a stressful meeting, imagine place cards in front of each participant with the names of famous heroes and villains. (Try comic strip characters for variety.)

Play the Polarities. Opposites are often humorous when placed together—soft and loud, big and little, expanded and contracted. Make a ceremony out of it! Mix ultraformal and sloppy casual (sneakers with formal wear, a baseball cap with your suit). Learn to dance back and forth between opposites. This may, on occasion, make it possible to find the elusive middle.

Find Some "Partners in Crime." Have you ever been to a joke-a-thon? You probably talk about current events, sports scores, or problems and difficulties with friends and family at home or colleagues at work. Why not share the funny things and get practice in remembering and telling jokes? Telling jokes, like laughing, is contagious. Once someone starts off with a joke, others are reminded of jokes they've heard. Creating a place to tell jokes is a big help in remembering them, as well as a great way to learn new ones.

Clip cartoons and paste them around the house or workplace. Send them in the mail to friends when you don't have time to write. In the midst of junk mail and bills, a cartoon is a welcome, loving message.
Change the Medium! TV's Marshall McLuhan said that the medium

is the message, so change the medium. Instead of saying it, make a picture, or sing it. Draw a billboard, wear a button. If you and your situation were a statue, what would the caption read? A picture is worth a thousand words, so put one in the place where you often get too serious, by the phone or over your bathroom mirror. This might cheer up the face looking back at you first thing in the morning.

Reframe. You know the expression: "When life gives you a lemon, make lemonade." Since there are no losses without gains, no joys without pain, humor can help us see the good that can come out of difficulties. In what situation would a particular experience be an asset? Maybe it's for the book you are going to write when your life gets interesting enough.

In front of a mirror, practice retelling a tragic event from your past. Intersperse the spice of humor as you elaborate the tale. Change the name of the central villain until you can tickle your funny bone. For example, if the man who "done you wrong" is named Dick, Dick becomes "Dicky," then "Sticky," then "Icky." If you are still having trouble smiling, put them all together. Every time you come across his name, as the plot thickens, refer to him as "Sticky-Icky-Dicky." If Linda left you in the lurch, let her be forever "Linda Lurch" or "Lurching Linda" in the memory modules of your mind.

AUTHOR REFLECTIONS

Sheila: I've always been an emotional, passionate person, but recent lessons from my own life experience have taught me to trust my emotions even more than I did when I was younger. In dealing with the loss of two of my three adult children and spending years writing about what helped and what didn't, I'm grateful to have had the support of women in my community to feel **all** of my feelings. I realized many men do not have that permission and support, and not having it makes the grieving process more difficult.

Now, as an expert on grief and loss, I write and speak about the art of grieving because grief, with its full palate of emotions, is something we do episodically, all of our lives. The way out is through, and our culture's habit of avoiding and shaming emotions and their expression, especially around sorrow, encourages depression, drug addiction, violence, and self-harm.

It's not true that if you start crying you won't stop, or, as we've told people who lose someone in tragedy, that the only way to honor the fallen is with hushed prayers and moments of silence. As the high school kids from the Parkland school shooting have shown us, a group's righteous anger focused to insure that others will not suffer the same fate creates a seismic force that changes the world. ❁

Christine: In regard to my personal self-care, I think the emotion piece has been the toughest. As a child, I was taught to "be nice," which translated to "only show happy emotions" and, something more damaging to self-care, "only allow yourself to feel the happy ones." I now know this, the suppression of all my feelings, was a big piece of the manifestation of my autoimmune disease. InterPlay was one of the tools that allowed me to be truly embodied, to notice what I was feeling. It gave me permission, and the skills, to ex-form and transform my emotions when needed. I've always been good at helping others express their feelings and now I'm good at expressing my own. ❁

SUMMARY

In living a self-care lifestyle we are affected by habits of the past, beliefs we have about ourselves and about how others view us, and the feelings and attitudes we bring to the helping situation. The dance of self-care in the emotional dimension involves . . .

Ignoring or denying bodily sensations ——

affects ability to receive and process kinesthetic information

leading to inaccurate perception of self and others

resulting in the negative emotions of fear, depression,

and resentment ——

Carrying around stored negative emotions results in ——

becoming DRAINED.

OR

Attending to bodily sensations ——

affects your ability to allow emotions to emerge from body

leading to being able to act on emotional messages ——

by gaining insight, making creative expression.

Reframing with humor or taking assertive action ——

results in becoming —— ENERGIZED.

I would only believe in a God who could dance.
—Friedrich Nietzsche

Renewing and Restoring: The Spiritual

The balanced life of spirituality is reached when we comfortably can hold together opposites
–Leo Booth, *Spirituality and Recovery*[1]

Sometimes our caring work doesn't have the outcome that we intended. Sometimes we take on too much of what belongs to another, wounding ourselves in the process. And there are times when, to renew and restore our spirits, those of us who help others need help ourselves.

Who Cares for the Caregiver?

"You and I are different, Sheila," Lois told me as we were finishing up our work together at the hospital. She had been a patient there for the past four months, and, though we had done some beautiful work together, I had my reservations about the safety of her being released at that time.

"You have taught me a great deal," Lois continued, "and I have always felt that you really cared. But you have been teaching me how to accept life on life's terms, and I don't want that. If I can't have life on my terms, I don't want it at all," she said firmly.

I still remember the feeling I had in my body during that conversation. It was as though someone had both hands on my spine and was twisting it in opposite directions, as if wringing out a beach towel. Lois taught me in that moment, more than anyone else ever had, the importance of taking care of myself, the importance of knowing and respecting my limits.

It wasn't yet noon the next day when I received the message that Lois had ended her life. Then, as now, in many places in our country, there were no effective limits on a former mental hospital patient purchasing a gun immediately upon their release. Through the sense of shock, horror, and disbelief, my husband and I reached out to each other. We had worked with Lois together for many months.

Next, we reached out to colleagues at our clinic. Forming a circle in one of the offices we, stood together and went into the *stillpoint*. We prayed silently for ourselves, for Lois, for her family and friends, and for the other caregivers who had worked so long and hard with her. Five minutes later, a staff member asked me to step into the group room for a moment. There, amidst a room full of singing people, I saw a cake lit with birthday candles, reminding me that it was my 50th birthday. As I caught my breath, I thought of a quote that used to hang on my office wall: "*Choose life, every wonderful, terrible, delightful, terrifying moment of it!*"

A Healing Ritual for the Healers

Lois's parents wanted to thank the hospital staff for all they had done for their daughter. In the midst of their own pain, they wanted the staff to know that they realized everything that could be done for their daughter had been done. This led to the idea of holding a memorial service for Lois at the psychiatric hospital, so that all those who had cared for her could participate.

During the ritual service, Lois's father shared an important message with Lois's doctors, nurses, therapists, and technicians, for all of us who work to help others. "Friends and family members have been asking us how this could happen after Lois had been in the hospital so long and so much had been done for her. Our answer is that if Lois had had cancer and had received all the most advanced treatments, she could have died anyway. If she had had a heart attack, she could have had a triple bypass—the most advanced technology—and she could have died anyway. The fact is, we all are only human, and what that means is that you can't save them all. Most people understand this when the problem is primarily physical, but the same is true for mental, emotional, or spiritual problems. You are not God."

The chaplain ended the brief service with an important message for everyone, especially those of us who work with ill and troubled people. He reminded us of the last words of advice Socrates gave to his students, just before he drank the hemlock: "Practice dying."

The Soma Twins on the Spiritual Dimension

I wasn't sure this was something the twins would want to deal with, but they had been so helpful in describing how they interact with the physical, mental, and emotional dimensions, I invited their comments. I told them that our scientific culture hasn't wanted to deal with the unseen world of the spirit. Priests and minister-types are allowed to discuss such matters, but when anyone else mentions the spiritual, it seems to trigger theological arguments or fears of voodoo and black magic.

Touchy began, "I'll never understand how *seeing* got to be so important for you folks. Nobody sees sound or heat waves, or atoms or germs with the naked eye, yet scientists are quite comfortable with these unseen phenomena."

Feelie joined in. "Restricting the spiritual dimension of life to churches, synagogues, and mosques has slowed down people's progress in understanding what it is to be truly human and what life is really all about."

I reflected, "I notice when I do body-oriented psychotherapy with some-one, when all the parts of the person are connected up and energy is flowing freely between all the parts, the person seems more than the sum of his or her parts. Spiritual themes emerge, suggesting to me that holiness is really wholeness."

Touchy added, "When people are in that self-transcendent place, they are able to carry out their sacred missions."

"And what is that mission?" I asked, more than a little curious to see how he would describe it.

"Each person's mission is to become who he or she truly is," Touchy said. "All ancient cultures used the body to experience the spiritual self. Through dancing, the use of chants, and be-coming aware of the breath (all ways to still the mind), the body becomes a kind of antenna, tuning in to subtler and subtler levels. When this happens often enough, the person finds direction and purpose, a place in connection to all of life and to the person's own path."

"Realizing where they have been, they know where they are going as well," Feelie said.

I remarked, "Years ago, when I was going through a divorce and feeling especially stressed, I worked with Barry Stevens, author of *Don't Push the River: It Flows By Itself.*[2] I needed help to let go of the struggle I was having accepting this reality of a divorce, and let go of the worry about what pain this might cause my children. As I dropped down into my own center, in the quiet of the moun-tains of western Colorado, a line from a Beatles song played in my ears: 'Let it be, let it be, there will be an answer, let it be.'"

Feelie smiled in recognition, "That is one of the songs that my inner wisdom sings to me, too."

"A client of mine got a powerful spiritual message when she tuned into her body. She was being mistreated by a coworker, and during a session to mediate their differences, she experienced a loss of hearing in her right ear. During a break in the session, her hearing returned. When the session resumed, her hearing difficulty returned. She had done a lot of prior work paying attention to her body and recognized that, in this situation, some part of her was trying to tell her something. As she listened carefully to her own inner voice she heard, 'Be still, and know that I am your God.' What turned out to be right for her was not to go along with the agreement that the people in her office were trying to arrange for her."

Both Touchy and Feelie were smiling and nodding agreement by this time. "You are describing the *stillpoint*," Feelie said.

"Yes," said Touchy. "Spiritual reality exists at the point where all things converge and connect. And you can get to that place when you need to by having practiced one of the disciplines of quieting the logical mind and heightening your sensory awareness. You can recognize the spiritual messages because they always take into account opposites—in other words, everything."

At this point, I asked Feelie to describe the stillpoint in her own words, but she assured me that T. S. Eliot had already done that much better than she could. She recited the following poem with deep emotion in her voice:

> *At the still point of the turning world. Neither flesh nor fleshless;*
> *Neither from nor towards; at the still point, there the dance is,*
> *But neither arrest nor movement. And do not call it fixity,*
> *Where past and future are gathered. Neither movement from nor towards,*
> *Neither ascent nor decline. Except for the point, the still point,*
> *There would be no dance, and there is only the dance.*[3]

An Army of Angels

It was the beginning of a workshop on self-care, and the leader, Ilana Rubenfeld, told the following story of an experience she had had in Brazil in the early seventies.

"I had been in a great deal of stress in my personal life and working very hard in my professional life. I began experiencing an odd symptom, numbness in the third and fourth fingers of each hand. I reasoned that if I'm doing something I really love passionately and I am getting sick or wounded, something is wrong. Since I was traveling in Brazil at the time, a friend suggested that I go to one of the traditional native healers for whom Brazil is famous. The message to me from the native healer was, "You are only one little person! There are too many who need your gifts. For what you are doing you need an army of allies in heaven, an army of angels!"

A Path of Pain

Later in the workshop, a 69-year-old man named Leonard asked to work with Ilana. The difficulty that he presented was a recurring pain in his back, which had been chronic for many years.

"I don't let it stop me from doing what I want to do, but I can't help wondering what my life would be like without it," he said. Since retiring from his job as an agency director, Leonard had enjoyed the fruits of his labors, living a full, active life. He and his wife traveled whenever their volunteer and community responsibilities allowed.

After gently touching his back, Ilana asked, with simple curiosity in her voice, "When do you first remember having the pain?"

"When I got out of the army in '45," was Leonard's crisp answer.

While continuing her gentle touching, Ilana asked, "Did anything special happen at that time?"

At this point, Leonard was in an easy state of relaxation, enjoying the experience of touch and talk. From this place, his answer seemed almost lackadaisical, "Nothing much. Just the usual stuff that happens in war."

The workshop participants, serving as witnesses to his work, responded with laughter as Ilana smiled and echoed his sentiments, "Nothing unusual, eh! Just regular war stuff, huh?"

After a brief pause, Ilana continued, "Is there anything that happened at that time that still feels unfinished for you? Something that may still be sitting there in your body that we could help you to let go of?"

Leonard responded with a blank look on his face. "I don't know."

"Start with anything," Ilana said continuing her gentle touching of his back muscles. "Just start with any old regular war stuff."

"I was in charge of troops. My troops liberated the concentration camps." His voice was without emotion, a reporter of facts.

A shift in the mood in the room became evident as the group responded to more than the facts he was relaying. I was seated across the room taking notes and moved closer to Ilana to offer moral support. As she continued her supportive touch she made an effort to take care of herself in relation to this difficult theme. She whispered to me, "Sheila, just wipe me off."

Sitting behind Ilana, I began moving my hands in the air, smoothing her aura, several inches from her body. This movement, which we sometimes refer to as an "energy wipe," created a flow within the energy field around Ilana and Leonard. When I continually repeated the movement that went from the base of Ilana's spine, the length of her body and upward towards the sky, my positive energy assisted Ilana in discharging the negative energy surging from Leonard through her. For all present, this kinesthetic reminder suggested that it was possible to direct the tension and energy of Leonard's releasing up, up, and away from our bodies.

As Ilana continued working with Leonard, I continued my *port de bra* (dance of the arms), moving the energy upward to the heavens and sometimes downward into the earth. Leonard's story unfolded, coming out of the releasing in his body. He related losing family members in the concentration camps. "Both my parents, my brother, sister, uncle, and cousins. I lost my whole family in the camps."

My thought: "I can't believe the US military would send a Jewish person to Germany, especially during Hitler's reign."

Ilana asked Leonard to describe his family, and he began to remember and relive pleasant times when the family members were together. He spoke of skiing with his father and other family members in Austria when he was growing up.

As he relived the pleasant memories, the muscles of his back began to soften. It seemed clear that he had not recalled and reclaimed these joyful, happy memories since his experience at the camps.

Ilana encouraged him, "You can remember skiing with your father and the others, the wonderful warmth and joy of the fun you and your family had together. These experiences belong to you, and you can go there anytime you want to remember all the wonderful gifts that your family gave you—all the gifts that can still be a part of you now."

The Message in an Image

From the movement that I was doing, I began to get an image of a guardian angel. As my arms moved in a flowing fashion behind Ilana, I remembered the pictures of guardian angels on the walls of the Catholic school I attended as a child. From this sensation of flight, I began to get an image of lots of angels. I remembered Ilana's earlier story about the Brazilian healer, and, reacting to Leonard's story, I whispered to Ilana, "I know who your angels are! There are six million of them at least. All the people from the concentration camps! They are surely an army of angels!"

As Leonard completed his work, in the peaceful reverie of family remembrances, he joined the group with the look of a child just waking from a nap. Ilana played a tape recording of a full orchestral version of a Viennese waltz. I remember thinking, as everyone in the room, including Leonard, began dancing, that dance therapist Marian Chase, the founder of dance therapy, was right, at some level: "Waltzing cures everything!"[4]

Leonard's work continued to reverberate throughout the rest of the week-long workshop, though not much was said about it in the group until the last day. As we began bringing our time together to a close, workshop participants of different ages and nationalities began dealing with the universal themes ignited for them by Leonard's work.

Contagious Feelings

Workshop members expressed gratitude to Leonard for allowing them to witness his letting go of his long-carried pain. This atmosphere of appreciation changed when a young German girl began to cry.

"I have so much shame! I feel so much guilt," she said with a heavy accent. "I know it makes no sense. I wasn't even born then, but it was my people that did those terrible things."

The group members sitting near the young woman reached out to her, putting their arms around her and supporting her. I moved behind the woman and the group members comforting her, and repeated my "guardian angel movements" as I had done with Ilana when she was working with Leonard. At this point I heard a voice from deep inside me that said, "No more victims! No more!"

No More Victims

Caregivers! Be aware of the lessons in Leonard's story:

If we store our reactions to horror and atrocity in our bodies, we keep the atrocities alive, interfering with our own vitality.

And

Working with people who are troubled or in pain is hazardous work. It takes a power greater than ourselves to keep us from taking into our bodies, and holding on to, the toxic realities.

Self-Care Skills in the Spiritual Dimension

Recounting my experiences with Leonard and Ilana and the young girl from Germany, I realize it was a turning point in my life. In that situation I saw clearly the exact nature of my vulnerability as a helping professional and my need for assistance in taking care of myself.

Recent work on the need to heal generational trauma[5] takes our human vulnerability further. When ancestors have been traumatized, these wounds can be transferred to the next generation through changes in the genes inherited. This creates more vulnerability as we deal with woundings in our own lives. Some people choose to deny harsh realities in order to protect themselves, but staying unaware increases the likelihood that we will become victims ourselves.

Sorting and Separating, the first self-care skill, needs to be done from a spiritual perspective. I do not know why bad things happen to good people or how people can be all but wiped out by others who believe they are doing the world a favor. Some things only God understands. All I can ask is, what does this mean for my own life? What am I here for? My prayer for myself in those moments is that I am able to stay present to the person in need of my help, so the person may learn the lessons from her or his own experience.

Using the second skill, *Letting Go*, began when Ilana assisted Leonard in letting go of the pain of his past. The rest of us had to *Let Go* of our reaction to his situation. Negative energy is magnetic, and some members of the group had special vulnerability to the theme of Leonard's pain. Jewish members, including Ilana, had to avoid taking on the victim pain. The young woman from Germany needed help in *Letting Go* of the shame she carried for the behavior of some of her German ancestors. Everyone's self-care choice: to remember the positive, mourn our losses, and reclaim our joy by joining in the dance.

The spiritual dimension is made up of *Partnership Power*. No one acts alone. Ilana used the power of the group as a healing circle around herself and Leonard. She asked for help from me, and I brought memories of guardian angels from my childhood and a suggestion that she send the pain to what the Brazilian healer called "an army of angels." Adding the spiritual dimension to our work and life means recognizing our connection to others, to one another, to those who have gone before us, and to the positive energy in the universe or to whatever name you give the God of your understanding.

The fourth self-care skill, *Stepping Back*, is illustrated when Ilana encouraged Leonard to step back from the ending of the lives of his family members to appreciate the gifts they had given him *during* their lives. And, for the group members and leaders, there was a balancing of the pain and negativity with the positive memories and the mutual support we gave to one another. *Stepping Back* enabled us to witness one man's pain while being supported by a caring community. From this emerged a commitment to live in such a way that we no longer become or create victims.

To *Exercise Choice* in the spiritual dimension we must remember that, as human beings, we are capable of heinous crimes as well as noble deeds. While facing the negative, we have the choice to despair or to focus on the positive lessons learned. If we do not take into ourselves the pain and atrocities of the past, we are free to create a better world for ourselves, for one another, and for those who will come after us. By way of taking care of myself and facing up to my own experiences of atrocities, I wrote the following poem:

A RECIPE FOR FORGIVENESS SOUP *
When it appears that bad things happen,
or have happened, to good people,
consider the following recipe for forgiveness soup.

Take at least:
two parts breath (as in keep breathing!), one part movement
(as in keep moving!), one part release (sometimes called prayer,
as in "Let go and let God!"),
Send it to the Army of Guardian Angels!
(That's what that heavenly host is for.)
Stir slowly all ingredients while humming your favorite lullaby.
As the pot starts to boil, season silently with smiles.
You will find your solution beginning to bubble with delight!

*When used as a trail mix, this soup will lighten your luggage and backpack. Especially recommended if you plan to travel through rough terrain or scale high places.

Embodying the Values of the Spirit

When we leave behind the hustle and noise of our busy lives, we often discover that our life situation doesn't match the values of our spirits deep inside. This incongruity can be scary and difficult to deal with. One way to connect more fully with your spiritual self is to identify more fully with your own value system. The following activity can help in the self-caring, self-healing journey of becoming and living the values of your spirit.

1. After a brief time of inner quiet, identify a universal value that is important to you. It could be honesty, humility, courage, generosity, justice, love . . . to mention but a few.

2. While remaining in a relaxed state, allow an image to emerge that represents the value you have selected.

3. Identify with this value by saying or writing, "I am (here name the value)."

4. Identify with your image by becoming that image. For example: Experience yourself as a bird to represent freedom, as a warrior to represent courage. Notice your feelings in the role of the person or object representing your treasured value.

5. Ask yourself, "Have I known the opposite value?" Write about that.

6. Ask yourself, "How do I deal with these values in my present life?" (Note: A variation that works better for some people is to work with the image before the verbal message.)

Let me offer the following example, working with one of the values closest to my own *stillpoint*, the value of justice.

From Injustice to Justice

When I was involved in a difficult, unequal relationship, I found myself using a lot of energy just maintaining my sense of self-respect. I was kept occupied by the continual need to confront the other person's manipulations and mistreatments of me. Periodically, the relationship would even out and work mutually well for a while, until the next storm, when I couldn't see any remnant of our past discussions or agreements. I worked on this relationship for several years because I loved the other person and I was dedicated to the work we were doing together. And, after all, nobody's perfect.

Finally one day, as I was meditating, I discovered that I had a soul hunger for justice. As I made this discovery, I knew that this hunger had been there all of my life and that I had a pattern of being in close relationships in which a just balance was impossible to achieve. For justice's sake (which is to say, my own sake) I had to leave what I loved. I finally realized that love cannot exist without justice. For us caregivers—helping professionals or informal caregivers of our children and our elders, nurses to the sick, teachers of the young, counselors to the troubled—justice requires that all parties flourish. And in that balanced equation lives love.

It is said that luck is a lady. Well, meet the lady Justice.

You've seen her standing in her Grecian robes, erect and tall. A blindfold covers her eyes and she is centered within so as not to be distracted by appearances. Under one arm she carries the book of knowledge acquired through the ages. In her left hand she holds a scale to weigh both sides in conflicts and disagreements. Since she is blindfolded, Justice cannot read the scale or become distracted by the appearance of things. She cannot read the expectations and opinions of others in their facial expressions or body postures. Justice must sense, from her own center, the subtle differences of weight on each side of the issue. Her own kinesthetic sense tells her the exact configuration, the exact point in time and space when the scales are in balance.

From that place of centeredness—that *stillpoint*—having let go of everything, Justice makes decisions that are right and fair and just. Staying in her own center, a place of clarity and love, Justice acts that all things may flourish in the fullness of time.

It may be helpful to understand what justice is *not*:

Justice is *not* what people are ready to accept.
Justice is *not* what people are comfortable with at a particular point in time.
Justice is *not* what people "think" is fair and just.
Justice is *not* what people have made a case for in the past.
Justice is *not* what I can persuade people to agree to.

I AM JUSTICE

I am justice!
I have taken my turn.
The sting of painful small injustices,
insults, taunts, and teasing putdowns,
sarcastic insinuations.
I've been slapped, shunned,
misunderstood,
wrongly accused.

I am justice!
I have paid my dues.
Watching powerlessly
other people's mistreatment.
Tall teacher humiliating my
trembling classmate.
Strapping father beating
my little brother.
Scolding mother threatening
through clenched teeth,
feeling sorrow, guilt,
embarrassment,
and shame.

I am justice!
I know the pain of
large-scale inequities,
help wanted signs:
"No blacks or Irish,
women or Mexicans
need apply."

I am justice!
I have done my homework.

Fine-tuning my breath,
standing up for myself,
joining hands with my
sisters, singing, dancing,
and letting go of
the pain.

The Spiritual and the Elements of Self-Care

In the spiritual dimension, attention is focused on the deep, inner self. The intention is for healing, for making whole. When we are coming from a place of balanced centeredness, we experience our connection to all that has gone before, to fellow travelers who share our journey, and to those who will follow after. Our attitude, once we involve the spiritual dimension, is one of wonder, curiosity, appreciation, and gratitude. These qualities of being in tune with what's happening spring from the experience of life as a gift. We no longer live in "hurry up" time but slow down to tune in to subtle levels.

Movement in the spiritual dimension involves surrendering completely to each phase of the dance, including the place of stillness. Nourishment for our souls comes from communing with nature, surrounding ourselves with beauty and order, in music and the visual arts, and participating in rituals that reinforce and express our values. Support comes from a loving community, from connection to ancestors and other spirit guides, and from the God of our understanding. Pleasure and play form connections between our child selves and our spiritual selves. Humor and rest enable us to keep a clear perspective, not taking ourselves or the events of our lives too seriously.

AUTHOR REFLECTIONS

Sheila: I was at the Pacific School of Religion in Berkeley, California, on a promotional tour for *Stillpoint* when the book first came out.

As I was passing the school's billboard filled with signs, "Apartment for Rent," "Free Cats," and "Need a ride to San Francisco?" an image of one of the school's teachers, dancing minister Cynthia Winton-Henry, called to me with a powerful force. I learned later that the poster was designed by Cynthia's work partner, another dancing minister and graphic artist, Phil Porter. These two "body intellectuals" had created together an improvisational system based in movement called InterPlay. Their integrative approach is spelled out in Phil's book, *Having It All: Body Mind, Heart, and Spirit Together Again at Last.* "We believe that spirit is a physical experience. Even though it may seem to be larger than us, we would not be able to recognize or identify spiritual experience unless there is something going on in our bodies."[6]

Cynthia's book, *What the Body Wants,*[7] is filled with stories of people, including me, who have gained life-changing value from their system. A dancing spiritual teacher, Cynthia explains that "while divine life doesn't require a religion, it needs a sanctuary, someplace to share what our bodies want and need through gracious, hospitable rituals of story, song, movement, and touch. InterPlay is such a place for those who seek freedom to be real, spontaneous, playfully affectionate, and open to truth. . . . I am as needy of the playful realm of embodied spirit as anyone." After getting this far in our book *Stillpoint*, you can probably see why, as a dancing social worker who'd been exploring and writing about self-care for many years, I jumped almost immediately into the deep end of what is now the international social movement InterPlay and my spiritual discipline. ✤

Christine: I am so grateful for the journey I have been on for the past twenty-five years. Meeting Sheila, watching her "dance" about self-care and self-healing at the NASW conference, and then being invited to a women's spirituality group at Earth Springs with my teacher Glenda Taylor[8] truly changed my life. Has it always been an easy one? No. But along the way, I have learned tools that have helped me to dance a full and authentic one. When I was going through graduate school in the early 2000s and had Dr. Brené Brown[9] for several of my social work and women's studies classes, I hit the jackpot. Between Brené and Glenda I learned how to deconstruct this material world and rebuild it with spiritual tools that encourage me to be connected and in the flow. InterPlay has also been a gift that shifted my work in the world to be more body-centered and whole-hearted. I use my labyrinth daily for meditation, reflection, and connection. My friend Cynthia Phelps,[10] an expert on self-compassion, reminds me to treat myself as I try to treat others when things go wrong, because of course they do. I laugh and remind my clients and myself, "People just keep showing up with their humanity."

SUMMARY

In living a self-caring lifestyle we are affected by habits of the past, beliefs we have about ourselves and about how others view us, and the feelings and attitudes we bring to the helping situation. Self-care in the spiritual dimension involves

Movement ——— involves surrendering into a place of stillness ——— leading to a discover of connection to people and values important to us becoming our true selves ——— resulting in moving from being DRAINED to becoming ENERGIZED.

Act Four

The Dance

*From the earliest of times, dance has been
a central part of creating community through
rituals, ceremonies, and celebrations.
In order for caregivers to not merely go through
the motions or mark time (as in a rehearsal)
but live more fully with joy and exuberance,
we need the support of a loving community.
Designing and performing rituals, we create
opportunities to come together and celebrate our
work, ourselves, and each other. When our rituals
are about peace and we join hands in dances that
celebrate who we truly are, each person flourishes
. . . and the world becomes a better place.*

*The dance—it is the rhythm of all that dies in order
to live again: it is the eternal rising of the sun.*
–Isadora Duncan

Reconciling and Re-creating Your Life

Let there be peace on earth, and let it begin with me.
–Sy Miller and Jill Jackson

The setting was a women's international peace conference, and a dark-skinned woman in ceremonial dress had taken the microphone. "The world doesn't have time to wait until everyone in the privileged countries achieves inner peace," she said in a powerful voice tinged with sarcasm.

"And I don't have time to wait for peace in my life until the politicians achieve world peace," I thought to myself.

The fact is, we human beings don't do well living in war zones. Peace may be a *prerequisite* for solving our personal, family, and global problems, not a *consequence*. Our psychobiology functions best when we can stay out of our survival mode. And we get along better with others when everyone can avoid pressing his or her panic button. Our wounds from prior hostilities need an environment of peace in which to heal. To become truly self-caring and self-healing means, in the end, to become a peacemaker.

Since both inner and outer peace are the best-case scenarios for people and all other living things, one would expect most everyone to be working to accomplish this glorious end. But peacemakers are not in oversupply in any country around the globe. Cities have trouble locating qualified peacemakers, churches and work organizations often run them off, and many families struggle to survive without a single peacemaker in residence.

It has been suggested that peace will not prosper until we clear up some small misunderstandings regarding its nature. With all the excitement generated by war, border skirmishes, and police actions, people have a tendency to think of peace as boring by comparison. Many people haven't yet discovered a peacetime equivalent to the good feelings generated by war-torn comrades sticking together to fight the enemy. Many people have difficulty marshaling their forces or conserving their resources unless threatened by someone they see as a fierce competitor. It's little wonder most of us haven't a clue about where to begin to achieve our own inner peace.

In the psychobiological model presented in this book, peace is the re-creation of balance and harmony among parts of ourselves, with our past and with the people in our work and home environments. When we rely only on what others seem to need or how it has always been done in the past, we experience anything but inner peace. Our job responsibilities may pressure us to spend more time at work while the needs of family members may be calling for our services. In the face of such competing demands, in order to achieve inner peace, we must find a way to consider our own needs along with the needs of others. Self-caring and self-healing are central to bringing about the reconciliation necessary for achieving inner peace—and eventually communal and global peace. As we practice the self-caring and self-healing actions in the four dimensions described in this book, we will find ourselves becoming peacemakers.

Once we achieve peace (not to be confused with boredom), we become engaged in a vigorous dynamic dance. In the process, each of us brings forth our very best. Once we've experienced peace, our whole system prefers it. However, peace is difficult to maintain. How can we continue to hold peace in our hearts as we rush through our days? Pushing ourselves to accomplish today's "to do" list, we oppress ourselves. When we are tired and drained from overextending and overdoing, we take it out on others. And when we are criticized? How peacefully do we handle people whose views deeply challenge our own?

As we continue practicing the skills of self-caring and self-healing while staying in connection to those we care about, we continually recondition ourselves for peace. As conflicting and contrasting parts of ourselves are integrated into a consistent, harmonious whole, we develop integrity. In fact, *integrity is the evidence that integration has taken place.*

By living our lives in a self-caring, self-healing way we take responsibility for bringing all aspects of ourselves into alignment. When physical, mental, emotional, and spiritual dimensions are in alignment, balance and harmony are achieved.

Building a Peacemaking Community

Consider our connections to one another; this balance and harmony cannot be achieved alone. We need each other. We affect one another. It is in peacemaking community with others that we each become who we truly are. Let's look at one of the most effective tools for building community—creating our own rituals. And let's remember—just as it is said the job can create the person, or people become what they do—together we create the community, and then the community creates us.

What words do you associate with the word "ritual"? Participants in a workshop on self-care suggested the following words: "ceremony," "transition," "change," "rite of passage," "solemn," "religious," and "continuity." Rituals are events designed to make experience special. My favorite definition of ritual came from one of my teachers, Anna Halprin: "Rituals are what love does to experience."

Rituals are part of the fabric of our lives. They are so woven into our everyday lives that we don't recognize the activities as rituals. Think about how we honor one another annually on the anniversary of the day we were born. In the United States the ceremony usually involves a cake, candles, and singing "Happy Birthday." Or think of particular family rituals such as setting a special place at the table for an honored guest, or the particular way in which Christmas presents are exchanged each year. Does everyone in the family open their own at the same time? Does one person have the honor of distributing them one at a time? In my father's family, gifts were stacked under each person's chair and, in spite of there being eight children, they took turns opening them one at a time.

Graduation and marriage are important times of change in people's lives, clear rites of passage, often celebrated with elaborate rituals. These ceremonies have elements of strong traditional symbols, which is probably why, in times of social change, people begin writing their own ceremonies. Their hope is that, by reflecting the new order of things, old symbols can be reclaimed and institutions can be renewed and revitalized.

To the casual observer, communal rituals may seem to belong more to indigenous cultures we've only read about, but our modern age has its share of ritual. Fourth of July parades commemorate a link to our historic past. In fact, most of our holidays are observed with ritual of one kind or another. Awards dinners, whether held at the local school or televised to the entire nation, celebrate outstanding accomplishments in sports, theater, and music. The entire world has become a global village, through the magic of technologies such as satellite transmissions and live-streaming. It's now possible to participate, at least as spectators, in the political, sporting, and religious rituals of peoples throughout the world.

Rituals always involve action, symbols, and other elements of good theater. Some are solemn and formal. Secular rituals may have strong spiritual elements, because rituals represent invisible and indescribable aspects of life. Rituals can be public or private, elaborate or simple. Rituals are designed to involve and transform the audience or witnesses as well as the people performing them.

As far as our self-care is concerned we must be aware that rituals can have their dark side. A ritual can be either a blessing or a curse. A family reunion may become an occasion to gossip about the people who couldn't (or weren't invited to) attend. A Friday night ritual get-together with coworkers can degenerate into an occasion for continually complaining about the boss.

Some of us elders may remember the horror of Jamestown, when hundreds of members of a religious community went to their deaths in a ritual of mass suicide. Members of neighborhood gangs have been known to carry out heinous crimes as part of group rituals or rites of passage. College fraternities have often crossed the line with life-threatening or life-ending hazing practices. Hitler's political rallies used ritual to build a community that would uphold the practices and principles of the Third Reich, replacing traditional ethical values and behavior.

The fact that something can be misused doesn't mean that we should avoid it altogether. It does mean that we need to look carefully at the rituals we are already participating in. Do these experiences support our health and well-being? It may look like love, but is it killing us with kindness? One organization I belonged to had enjoyable gatherings where people sang and swayed together, but the members had no real say in the design of the rituals or in the organization. Ultimately participation in the rituals of this organization reinforced our role as children relying on a single leader.

Taking responsibility for our lives as true grown-ups means refusing to participate in rituals that do not empower us and contribute to our own and the community's greater good. It means learning to use ritual to create and build the kind of community we need for our mutual self-caring and self-healing.

A Simple Ritual for Peace

At a professional meeting in New York several years ago, a man led the group in a thirty-second ritual, which he had received in Germany from someone who got it from the Gandhi Foundation in India. I began teaching it to my staff and start each staff meeting and therapy group I led with it. I noticed the powerful effect it had on me and the other group members, and how it set a tone of peace and reconciliation.

A year later I was asked to participate in the planning committee for an international women's peace conference in Dallas, Texas. I brought the ritual with me and we decided to use it to open the conference proceedings each morning. Each day a different group of women, representing their own nationality, performed the gestures and words from the stage in their own native language. Audience members, standing in front of their seats, followed along with them. Each day we revisited the copy machine to make more copies as the women expressed their wish to take it back to the 65 countries they represented. I've often wondered, from that conference, how many people have shared this ritual in how many countries, and what has been the outcome? Like the soft drink commercial with the song about teaching the world to sing "in perfect harmony," we can hope this type of activity conditions us for peace and will continue to do so.

A UNIVERSAL GREETING

This Universal Greeting from the Gandhi Foundation is easy to learn. Place this book where you can read it and yet have both hands free. Think of someone with whom you need to have reconciliation. Imagine saying the words and making the gestures to that person. Or perhaps you need to start off in front of a mirror, sending this message to yourself. As you say the words, perform the gestures: they are based on universal sign language and move beyond the barriers of verbal languages. Allow yourself to experience the movements as a graceful dance. Later teach this greeting to a group of people who are interested in working together in a spirit of peace.

I OFFER YOU PEACE
(*Face palms forward, elbows bent*)
I OFFER YOU FRIENDSHIP
(*Cup hands palm to palm, elbows bent*)
I OFFER YOU LOVE
(*Draw hands forward from heart*)
I HEAR YOUR NEEDS
(*Cup hands behind ears*)
I SEE YOUR BEAUTY
(*Cover eyes with hands, then uncover*)
I ACKNOWLEDGE YOUR FEELINGS
(*Arms cross chest, fingertips to shoulders*)
MY WISDOM FLOWS FROM A HIGHER SOURCE
(*Right arm moves in an arc from behind the head to meet upturned left palm at chest level, fingertips forward*)
I SALUTE THAT SOURCE IN YOU
(*Palms together in prayer position*)
LET US WORK TOGETHER
(*Fingers interlocked as two-handed fists pointed upwards*)

The Ritual of the Cornbread

One of the most powerful rituals I've ever experienced happened because of some cornbread. I was living in the eastern part of Nebraska, coordinating a project for human service workers in the western part of the state. The goal of the project was to learn more about the Native American and Mexican American cultures in and near Scottsbluff and to improve the delivery systems attempting to help them meet their needs.

I invited a Native American professor of fine arts to accompany me to the project site and give a guest lecture in the course I was organizing. The woman, Gaylyn, who lived on the East Coast, told me she could accept my invitation if I could get her some cornbread. She explained that on the date we were discussing, she would be coming off her monthly fast. According to her native traditions, fasts are broken by cornbread. I asked the Native American women in Nebraska for help in getting the cornbread, but they seemed concerned about what kind of cornbread would be appropriate. As members of a different tribe from Gaylyn's, they were aware that each tribe is likely to have its own recipe for this important staple. When I asked Gaylyn, she laughingly said, "Any kind will do, just so it's cornbread."

Gaylyn and I traveled by plane and then car to the hotel and workshop site. Time seemed to go by quickly as we shared our stories and got to know each other better. She was learning more about me and the project I was coordinating, and I was learning more about her and her life and culture. That evening, after Gaylyn's presentation, several women came forward with the important cornbread. As we thanked them, I noticed they seemed honored to have been asked to provide it.

Gaylyn and I went back to the quaint little hotel in the center of town where we each had a room. As we were saying goodnight, Gaylyn surprised me by asking if I would like to join her in her room to witness her ritual. I remember experiencing the same feeling of gratitude as had the women who had baked the corn bread. I felt honored—and a little scared that I wouldn't know how to act.

Thirty-plus years have passed since that night in her hotel room, but tears come to my eyes each time I remember it. She had a pipe and some other sacred objects, and I remember her praying out loud and allowing the smoke from the pipe to trail into each of the four directions. Many details of what she did and said are hazy to me now, but I will never forget the feelings of blessedness that I had as I witnessed her ritual.

She prayed for the project, that it would serve the native people. She expressed gratitude for the women who had made the cornbread. And then she prayed out loud—for me. She understood, as I did not, that my being in that leadership role as project coordinator would transform me. She asked that I be given the courage to listen to the people and to serve them. The ritual ended as I dried my eyes and we broke cornbread together.

We spent several other days together later on, working on the project. I remember a postcard from her . . . and later a Christmas card I sent, but we lost track of each other long ago. I remember telling my students how close I still feel to this woman after all these years. It's as though we are relatives.

I've come to understand that such is the power of ritual. Though we shared many thoughts and ideas and told each other stories of our backgrounds and cultural experiences, it was the ritual that made us sisters forever.

Designing My Own Rituals

After my experience with Gaylyn's cornbread ritual, I began to develop a new appreciation for the power of ritual. Native Americans, in living with ritual, set a strong example of how ritual helps us to appreciate the sacredness of all of life and how to bring that notion into our everyday consciousness.

A Wedding Ceremony

When we married in 1979, my husband and I designed our own wedding ceremony, a practice that has become more common now. We bought a book that explained the meaning of the symbols and practices of a traditional wedding. This way we could decide what parts we wanted to include in order to affirm certain values—and what needed to be eliminated as not representing what marriage meant to us. Since we were from different religious traditions, we purposefully included aspects of each to signify a blending of our two traditions. Because of the differences in our family backgrounds, no one in either family was particularly pleased with our marriage. Family members on both sides came to the ceremony with much trepidation, taking each of us aside in turn, making suggestions and requests regarding the ceremony. Warnings of impending doom were also communicated should we do (or not do) certain things.

Fortunately, the minister who had agreed to preside had not only given us free rein—"Just write out what you want me to say"— but he also told us: "In my experience, once the ceremony happens, the struggle is over and no one remembers the fears." He seemed to be saying that the ritual would work its own magic.

I'm not sure we believed him, but we proceeded as though we did. In our wedding ritual, using a form from Universal Dances for Peace, our family members danced and sang together. And when the inner circle of the dance (my family) joined with the outer circle (his family), a union of two very distinct families was accomplished as well. My daughter sang, my sons poured the wine, and everyone danced and cried.

One family member said the ceremony stayed with him for days. "It was so powerfully emotional," he said. I still do not understand how, but, in effect, all relationships were different from that day forward. Had we known that would happen, we might have arranged to have the ritual sooner, rather than waiting several years for the courage to do it.

A Career Ritual

Many years later I stumbled into designing my own personal ritual. This was not for a traditional occasion like a wedding, but rather on an occasion that normally would *not* be celebrated at all. And I wasn't really thinking I would *do* the ritual, I just jotted notes in my journal and thought about it, and this gave me great strength and pleasure through a difficult time.

I had traveled to New York to work on a writing project. Just before I left Texas, my university boss (and mentor of six years) told me that he had changed his mind and would not be supporting me for tenure. This betrayal was a total shock to me and to everyone involved, since I had gotten an eight-to-one vote from my social work colleagues in favor of my tenure request. I arrived at my hotel room and set up my computer, and as I typed the words, "A Healing Ritual," I began to heal.

I visualized the ritual; I saw the scene, the people, and the place. I heard the music. I began typing a description of what was going on inside my head. As the words flowed out from my fingers, feelings of relief moved throughout my entire body. My spirits lifted as I laughed at the satire of a funeral I was designing for my university career.

In the months that followed I handled the treachery that continued to be played out by rewriting and rereading my ritual. This was a wonderful way to step back for a broader perspective and to keep a clear distinction between the death (murder, really) of my career, and my own continuing aliveness. Later it became evident that, for my own healing, I needed to actually perform the ritual. I sent the following invitation to my friends, family, and professional colleagues:

Iatreia Institute for the Healing Arts in cooperation with
The Mini Mouse School of Social Work
and
The Center for Women Who Work Too Much
Presents
SHEILA K. COLLINS' TRANSFORMATION
OF A CAREER: A HEALING RITUAL
Saturday, September 5th, 7 pm
Reception to follow ceremony

The actual text of the ritual is included in appendix B as an example and an act of encouragement to all of you who have (or will) experience career dissolution, betrayal by colleagues and friends, or simple disappointment upon the death of a dream.

Designing Your Own Rituals

Career situations are not the only type of situations that can benefit from ritual. Life-changing events such as divorce, retirement, relocation, or moving, to name a few. In any situation of major life change, a ritual can be a powerful tool for self-caring and self-healing. Consider the following worksheet to help you collect the various elements needed for your own ritual.

RITUAL-PLANNING WORKSHEET

1. Identify the *situation* in your life that calls for constructive change.
2. Describe yourself in the *old* situation or state.
3. Describe yourself in the *present* situation or state.
4. Describe yourself in the *new* situation or state that you are moving towards.
5. As you move into this new phase of your life, list what you intend to

   Take With   Leave Behind   Develop New

6. (*The Score*) On a single sheet of paper describe what you will do in each phase. Include time and space for each phase—the beginning, the middle, and the end.

RESOURCES FOR THE CEREMONY

People—Consider the people you want involved and what roles you want them to play. You may want to allow a time for people you have invited to say a few words as is done at memorial services or, in a lighter vein, at roasts. Give clear directions. Remember, "This is your life!" This is your party, and you can cry and laugh whenever you want to.

Readings—Think of scenes from literature, classic myths, or fairy tales. The main idea here is to tap into the universal theme of your situation as it may have been treated by classical writers. This will help you to see your personal tragedies and triumphs from a larger perspective.

Music—Select anything, from opera to musical comedy to folk to country to popular. They will all work, depending on the metaphors you want to use. Singing is a wonderful way to involve certain people—or the witnesses as a whole.

Symbols/Objects—Think of archetypical objects, objects that carry strong meaning in most cultures: fire, water, light, bells, and drums. A filing cabinet and a bonfire were used in my ritual. Gaylyn used a pipe and other objects sacred to her culture's traditions.

Movement—Think of a way to represent the movement that you are making in your life. Rituals are always about moving from one situation or state of being to another. Processions and dancing offer ways for the audience to become participants with you in your ritual.

Rituals in the Home

It isn't necessary to wait for big events like weddings or funerals to experience a ritual. Events in a particular family member's life can be a time to pull out your ritual-planning worksheet. Mother's promotion at work, Dad's winning golf score, a teenager's first driver's license, a youngster's overcoming failing grades at school—these are all occasions made more special by a celebration. Planning a ritual just makes it more conscious and purposeful.

AUTHOR REFLECTIONS

Christine: For birthdays in our family we have the ritual of breakfast in bed. Cards that come in the mail are saved for the actual morning. A tray is created with the recipient's favorite breakfast foods; a couple of flowers are cut from the yard and artfully arranged. Family members start the birthday person's special day by gathering together and beginning to sing while bringing the tray containing cards, presents, and food into the birthday person's bedroom.

A more frequent ritual we do is a blessing of our home once a week. We clean for an hour as a family, which includes the vacuuming, dusting, and chores we don't do daily. We make it a ritual by the music we put on and the candles we light, and then at the end we smudge the entire house to clear the energy in addition to the dust.

Personally, I have a daily ritual of greeting the sun by walking my labyrinth. I do a walking meditation and think of everyone that is on my prayer list. I often sing my prayers, which include a song I learned years ago at Glenda Taylor's EarthSprings Retreat Center in Crockett, Texas, from my friend Christina. Each verse alternates with people in the parentheses:

> For all the _____ (children, teachers, parents, world) wherever you may be,
> For all the_____(children, teachers, parents, world) however you may be,
> I wrap you around with infinite love and wisdom.

Then I take a few moments in the center of the Labyrinth to be quiet and listen. This ritual takes me to my place of balance and a well of calmness that I can access throughout the day as needed. ❁

Short, less formal rituals can have a big effect on family life. One family I knew had the philosophy that each child deserves some time each week to be an "only child." In spite of having nearly a dozen children, they arranged a weekly walk, a trip to the store, or a talk on the porch swing for each child alone with dad and then time alone with mom. When children are small this special time can happen at bedtime. Remember, one definition of ritual is "what love does to make experience special."

Events that affect the whole family, such as a move to another state or a divorce, are not usually marked by ritual. Yet, it is in situations of dramatic change such as these that rituals can be powerful tools for healing both individuals and the family as a whole. If it fits with your religious values, you might consider asking a minister or priest to formally bless your new house or participate with your family in a ritual of forgiveness to help the family move through a divorce.[1]

Workplace Rituals

Think about the organization where you work, and begin to notice the rituals already going on there. How are staff members' birthdays celebrated? What about coffee breaks? Company picnics or the Christmas party? How are people rewarded for an outstanding performance or honored for years of service? More than likely there are rituals that have sprung up over the years for these and other special occasions.

Make sure these practices reflect the values you want to encourage in yourself and others. One woman whose job involved long hours sitting at a computer told me, "At our company, whenever we do something good, they feed us!" She was referring to the staff luncheons and breakfasts and award banquets that made it very difficult for her to maintain a healthy weight. All the rituals at her workplace involve sweet and fattening food and most people gain 10 pounds the first year they are employed there.

A man I knew had to leave his job for health reasons because all the in-service and training events involved extensive "happy hours" with the booze flowing freely. High performance was rewarded by many toasts to the honored guests, and excessive overworking was encouraged as the norm in demonstrating loyalty to the "company store."

On a more positive note, at one workshop I led on self-care for executives of social service agencies, a lively discussion revealed how these managers and directors were already structuring time for positive workplace rituals. They use special occasions for enjoyable time together to build skills in teamwork and collaboration. Take the example of a new staff member or student trainee joining an established group. The meeting begins with a question each staff member is invited to answer. The question is different each time, but it always has something to do with each person's relationship to his or her work. The question might be, "When did you first know you wanted to do the work you are now doing?" or "How are you the same or different at work from how you were in your family growing up?" "Who is the person who most influenced your work and how?" While providing the newcomer with an interesting way to get acquainted with the staff, this ritual gives long-term staffers a new look at one another.

A New Beginning

An owner/manager of an insurance agency enlisted my help in designing a ritual for the opening of his small agency's new offices. The company had been through a major reorganization with many difficult physical and emotional changes. He wanted to recognize what the agency and its employees had been through in recent months, to celebrate the new office, and to look forward together to an exciting and challenging future. A memo was sent to employees announcing this special event and enlisting their participation in the planning. Each person was asked to fill out the following worksheet.

1. In making the move to new offices, list anything you hope to leave behind.
2. List anything you want to be sure to bring along.
3. What are you especially looking forward to at the new location?
4. Do you have a specific contribution you would like to make to the festivities? Describe.
5. In the spirit of improving the office environment, what "rules" would you like to suggest for the agency?

6. Are there any "rules" that you feel have been operating in the present that you would like to see eliminated? Describe.
7. Name any music that you feel would be particularly appropriate for this occasion.

Material from these worksheets was compiled into "Leaving Behind and Bringing with—A Litany," recited with the theme from "Raiders of the Lost Ark" playing in the background. The following new rules of the house were constructed and sung as in a Gregorian chant:

Rules of The House

There will be no smoking, chewing, spitting, and drinking of alcoholic beverages on these premises.

Employees and associates will check their bad moods in the parking lot and smile upon entering the front door.

Employees and associates will notify the establishment of their whereabouts whether in or out, or when due to return to the office.

Language at this agency shall be at all times fit for polite company, not offensive to gentlemen, ladies, and innocent minors.

Using all proper forms, work submitted by 9 shall be out by 5.

Employees and associates, remember: Reality is not always the way you see it, so respect others' points of view.

Warning: Should these rules be broken, serious consequences shall befall the offender, as the establishment is henceforth serving notice—No More Nice Guy!

The Finale

Caring for others is a hazardous occupation, made less so when we have learned to care for and heal ourselves. The state of the world can get better only when we learn to use what life is presenting us as fuel for our fire, breath for our song, and energy for our dance. Rituals can help us celebrate our connection to one another and build the community of support necessary for each of us to take care of ourselves. Like the chick emerging from its shell, the snake shedding its skin, and the caterpillar becoming the butterfly, self-caring and self-healing require transformation to mature adulthood, all the while nurturing the ancient child within.

We stop ourselves so often from joining in the dance. A participant at the international peace conference in Dallas showed me how to courageously break through reservations and unreasoned fears, and this led to an unexpected and transforming finale.

My presentation was a peace dance in the lounge of the student center where the conference was held. Conference participants were seated around the room informally, as artists from different countries performed for them and for one another. As I was in the middle of my dance, a dark-skinned woman I didn't know jumped up from her seat. In ceremonial dress she joined me for a most joy-filled duet. I did not know her country or her language, but a sense of deep understanding passed between us as we danced together spontaneously. Later, a friend told me of the conversation that occurred prior to our dancing together.

The woman in the colorful dress said to her companion as they watched me dance, "Oh, I feel so inspired to join her."

Her companion said, "You can't do that. You're too fat!"

Disregarding her companion's protest, the woman, recognizing a shape that I was assuming in my dance, said, "That's like yoga; I know this. Of course I can!" and she proceeded to act on her inspiration by joining me in my dance.

And you too can join in the dance by creating and performing your own rituals and transforming your own life. As a director or team leader you can use ritual, not only to assist employees with their self-care, but to transform your workplace and the work done there. Include rituals of self-care that balance the essential elements of movement and still-ness, work and play, pleasure and pain, and experiences of connection and solitude.

Practice the skills of self-caring and self-healing by doing your own *Sorting* work, *Letting Go and Surrendering*, and don't forget the duet— *Building and Using Partnership Power*. At those crucial points, *Step Back* for a broader perspective, and always and continually, *Exercise Choice*. From the *stillpoint* of our inner world may each of us transform our caring dance from one that *drains* us to one that *energizes* as we grace-fully express who we truly are.

Epilogue,
Revised Second Edition

Caregivers are not immune to illness or needing care themselves. As I've been working on this revised version of *Stillpoint*, Jyoti King, an important contributor to the first version, dear friend, nurse, and former manager of our clinic, has seemed close at hand. The African expression "*I am because you are*" says everything about who Jyoti was, and still is, in my life and in the lives of many others. A lifetime caregiver, Jyoti suffered from episodes of environmental illness most of the years I knew her, and then the most dreaded of diseases, Alzheimer's. Her life and the long goodbye journey that it became illustrate most all of the points in this book, particularly the way the community holds us when, as individuals, we falter.

As I write her name, images come to me.

We're holding one another in a tearful embrace for the second time around. One year earlier my son had been diagnosed with AIDS, and now, her son. "Perhaps we are carrying this sisterhood thing too far," one of us says. (*Partnership Power*)

After a misunderstanding at the clinic, we stand together with our teacher Glenda Taylor in a ceremony of reconciliation while others involved in the situation stay away. (*Letting Go and Surrendering, and the Power of Ritual*)

I become the first person Jyoti invites to accompany her on a visit to the mother she barely knows. We enter a mental hospital where her mother has been confined since shortly after Jyoti's birth. (*Letting Go, Sorting and Separating, and Partnership Power*)

Standing in Jyoti's office as we discuss personnel difficulties at the clinic, I note the ever-present framed picture of her guru on her desk. (*Surrender and Step Back for a larger perspective*)

Sitting in the parlor of the memory care center, I ask her to bless the manuscript of my then unpublished book *Warrior Mother*. She takes the binder from me and, entering the *stillpoint*, she holds it prayerfully to her heart. (*Power of Ritual*)

On what turns out to be my last visit, I come upon her alone in the memory care community room, rocking in a rocking chair and singing to herself, a boot-scooting Texas song. (*Self-care, Self-compassion, and Exercising Choice*)

It's often said it takes a village to raise a child, but the life and legacy of Jyoti underscores for Christine and me that it takes a village of people showing up for one another to make it through the challenges life is likely to send us all. Jyoti demonstrated how to be a graceful caregiver and a graceful receiver of care, something caregivers often find hard to do. We wish for all caregivers the kind of loving support that Jyoti received from a community of people who recognize who you are at the soul level, and who will sing your song back to you, even if you have forgotten its words.

Epilogue (original)

The dance changes the dancer. The practice of the technique changes the dancer's body, the rehearsal changes the dancer's mind and emotions, and the performance changes the dancer's spirit. Caregiving done as a dance, wholeheartedly with one's body, mind, emotions, and spirit, transforms the caregiver.

And sometimes this transformation comes late in one's life, after other careers have ended. I learned of this firsthand from my own parents. During the three years or so of my mother's terminal illness, my father became her caregiver. She had been a nurse—always a caregiver of others. Driving in the limousine to the cemetery we family members tried to name all the different people mother had taken into our house. She collected stray, needy people like children sometimes collect stray, needy animals. Mother had always worried about my father and how hard he worked. She believed, and even had us convinced, that she would end up taking care of him.

It seemed a strange role reversal. Dad, the engineer, became my mother's nursemaid. Dad, who rarely took even an aspirin himself, kept track of mother's many medications and told her which pills to take and when. And since Mother was unable to carry out her usual caregiving chores, Dad took over her route, standing in for her with friends and neighbors. Though not a Catholic, he started going to Mass with mother every week, something he never did when we were children. Nothing in his early life growing up on a farm, or later on, in his training and experience as an engineer, had prepared him for this new career as a caregiver.

I didn't see it on a daily basis; I lived too far away. But when I came to visit I would see the changes in them both. My mother, growing sicker and more dependent, struggled with the unfamiliar and often uncomfortable role of receiver rather than giver. She would fight him, determined to preserve some semblance of her former independence.

The changes in my dad were pronounced, too. He gained some weight and often looked tired. But he seemed softer, happier to see us, and more talkative. I noticed that his eyes would moisten with tears when he mentioned something that was important to him. This happened on the day I realized that the role of caregiver had changed him.

We were talking about the changes in the Catholic liturgy and how much better it was that the priest now spoke in English. He mentioned the blessing at the end, when the priest would usually turn to the congregation and say, "God be with you. Go in Peace!" One particular day the priest changed the wording of the blessing to "God be with you. Go and *serve* one another!" My father had tears in his eyes as he told this to me, and he followed it with a comment, said in his own unique style: "And baby, that's what it's all about!"

Acknowledgements, Revised Edition

Inspiration and encouragement to do this revised second edition came from two coaches in the Quantum Leap community, Martha Bullen, and Geoffrey Berwind; Victoria Campbell, who was involved in the first edition; and coauthor Christine Gautreaux, who admired *Stillpoint* and has found it useful through the years. They all believed it was a good idea to update the book and make it available for a new generation of caregivers. The idea appealed to me especially because it was the opportunity to include practices and people that have come into my life since the first *Stillpoint* was published. I met Cynthia Winton Henry and Phil Porter, the founders of InterPlay, on my first trip to promote *Stillpoint*. They welcomed me into their playful creative body wisdom practice and community, allowing me to join my vision and efforts to theirs as we've worked and played together these past 25 years. Having the support of playmates has been the very best self-care, making all the difference in my ability to take care of myself as I was caregiver to two of my three children and best friend, through their illnesses and deaths. I offer deep appreciation to Cynthia and Phil and the InterPlayers I've collaborated and co-created with around this country and internationally. They are a part of all of my creative accomplishments, including this one.

AUTHOR REFLECTIONS

Christine: I'm filled with gratitude for Sheila and her trailblazing as a wise, dancing social worker. I'm especially thankful for our twenty-year friendship and sisterhood, which might not have happened without our teacher, mentor, and friend Glenda Taylor. Special thanks to the friends and family who supported me during this process, my Manifesting Mondays group, accountability partners, and the Atlanta InterPlay community. Revising a book does truly take a village. To my dancing husband, Joe, thank you for tucking me in at night when I was past done. Your support has been invaluable. To our daughters Alex and Sammie, as I see you growing into strong, beautiful young women who will make a difference in the world, I hope this book reminds you to take care of yourselves along the way. ❖

Christine and I owe incredible gratitude to Martha Woolverton and Debra Heirs for their editing genius and to Christy Collins for her artistic skills and for putting us in touch with artist Mara Friedman, whose artwork graces the cover of this book. We also owe special thanks to Joe Gautreaux, Christine's husband, for his delightful illustrations of the Soma Twins. Many thanks to all our supporters and the whole team for collaborating with us in such a true partnership way. As we take a moment to pause, take a deep breath, and reflect on the joy and gift that working on this book has been, we want all *Stillpoint* readers to know, "*We wrap you around with infinite love and wisdom.*"

Acknowledgements (original)

Throughout the long, difficult process of birthing this book, many people provided invaluable assistance, encouragement, and inspiration. For their help with the stillborn version that preceded this present volume, I wish to thank Ilana Rubenfeld, Joan Lakin, Jim Collins, and Florence Korzinski, along with the 1984–1988 Rubenfeld Synergy Method training community, who acted as fair witnesses to the emerging dancer / social worker struggling to become writer.

Colleagues in the helping professions who read the early drafts included Drs. Roy Martin, Jean Deschner, and Coleen Shannon, and student Laurel Chapet. I am grateful for their support and suggestions.

For help with the first edition I wish to thank Ian Jackson, who taught me some of what he knows about editing, and who shared his Breathplay and hypnosis work with me. Frances Townsend, a multi-talented woman, worked many hours with me on editing. She also shared with me some of her vast knowledge of nutrition and how to become self-caring with food.

Special appreciation goes to the members of the Live Poets' Society: Dr. Gary and Victoria Campbell, Randall and Jyoti King, and Dr. Richard Citrin for forming a community around me when I was feeling most alone, and teaching me that writing, too, can be a dance.

Additional appreciation goes to Bertha Hendricks and Roy Martin for their help with the final editing phase.

I owe the deepest gratitude to my family, my husband, Richard Citrin, and children, Corinne, Kevin, and Kenneth, who supported me through the roller-coaster rides of my career life and through many of the events on which this book is based.

Finally, and most especially, I wish to acknowledge and express my gratitude to two outstandingly powerful and brilliant women without whom this volume would never have been completed. Jyoti King and Rosa Marie Meile stayed beside me, editing, encouraging, and continuing to believe in me and this work, even through the periods of my deepest discouragement. They, and many others unnamed, have taught me the true meaning of partnership power.

Appendixes

APPENDIX A

As we hear that sitting is the "new smoking" as far as health and well-being are concerned, the question then becomes, what kind of movement practices or activities do we need to engage in? Here are some suggested possibilities to help you be more in touch with your body and to help your body to get what it needs and wants.

Movements for Mending

I. Breathplay

Taking control of your breathing is a powerful way to take control of your life. Ian Jackson, a colleague of mine, has written a whole book on this subject, but let me suggest one of his most powerful techniques, one he calls Upside Down Breathing. This technique reverses what we normally do when we get anxious and try too hard. After some practice, this technique can be done standing, sitting, or while driving a car or riding a bus, but let's begin by lying on the floor.

1. Get comfortable on the floor, on your back. Place your hands on your lower belly and press in as you exhale.
2. After you have exhaled all your air, release your hands and allow air to come back into your lungs automatically.

3. Next, actively press your lower belly again, expelling all your air.
4. Release your hands and stay passive as the air rushes back into your lungs.
5. Appreciate that your job is letting go of the old air and that new air comes to you automatically when you are able to make room for it.

II. Metaphorical Breathplay

Ian and I have found the power of this simple breathing exercise to be greatly enhanced by adding imagery and the intention of healing as you perform the movements.

1. Think of something in your real life that you would like to let go of or eliminate from your life.
2. As you breathe out, create an image that you are eliminating what you have selected in step 1.
3. As you relax to allow air to reenter, picture taking into yourself something that you need more of in your life.
4. Keep an open mind to these new possibilities, and notice any changes in your life after a week or so of practicing these movements.

III. Polarity Play

This activity comes from the field of dance therapy. I've used it so often I've forgotten who should get credit for it. I know it to be a wonderful way to escape the limitations of an either/or view of the world. Playing frequently with these possibilities will help you get unstuck and teach you respect for the wisdom of your own body.

1. Select two opposite (or what seem to be opposing) qualities. You may use tension/relaxation, giving/receiving, courage/fear, strength/weakness, or select self-caring elements you are having trouble bringing into balance. (See list in chapter 1.)

2. Create a gesture or movement to represent the first quality you have selected. Perform this movement.

3. Now create a movement to represent the second quality and perform this movement.

4. Moving in slow motion, perform the first movement, followed by the second.

5. Continue going back and forth between the two movements.

6. Notice if the movements change in any way as you perform them in this manner. Allow this to happen by simply following the movement and going where it "wants" to go.

7. Your reward for suspending any judgment or opinion that this is "foolish" or "doesn't make sense" will be your discovery of your body's way of creating harmony and balance in the physical dimension.

8. Reflect on what this information might mean in other areas of your life.

9. Thank your kinesthetic senses for this gift of wisdom.

IV. One-Hand Dance

This movement form comes from InterPlay. By going through some simple possibilities first, when you finally begin to move with the music, you may be able to relax more fully and allow your hand to make the "choices." This activity can induce a trance-like state in the mover and has been used often with patients in a hospital or hospice setting. It can also be done "on behalf of someone else," as a kind of prayer form. You may lie down, sit, or stand, whichever is more comfortable and appropriate for you.

1. Bring one hand into the air.

2. For 30 seconds, do some smooth movements with your hand.

3. Now do smooth and fast.

4. For 30 seconds do some jerky movements.

5. Now do jerky and slow.

6. Make a shape with your hand and hold it.
7. Make another shape . . . and another . . . and another.
8. Bring your hand in contact with your body or the floor or your chair.
9. Move your hand to another point of contact.
10. Now take us as much space as you can with one hand. Find out how far your arm can go.
11. Take a deep breath and let it out with a sound.
12. Now put on a piece of music and play around with the movements of one hand.
13. (After the music) What did you notice?

V. Mudras (Ritually Symbolic Gestures)

A man goes to his priest (rabbi, minister) and reports his discomfort in no longer believing in the faith of his youth. He would like to become a believer again, but he doesn't know how. The spiritual leader gives him a simple prescription: "Each day assume the posture of prayer and behave as though you have the faith that you seem to have lost. We are built in such a way that we become what we do."

1. Assume a kneeling position. Place palms together in front of your body with fingers pointing upward.
2. Begin slowly raising your hands upwards towards the sky. Allow your face and neck to follow your hands.
3. When you have reached the extent of your range in this direction, slowly lower your hands.
4. When your hands have returned to the level of your heart, begin sitting back on your feet.
5. Bending from your hips, begin separating your hands and reaching out towards the floor in front of you (similar to the child's pose in Yoga).
6. Surrender your weight to the floor as you surrender your will to your Higher Power.

7. Stay in this place of surrender until you feel compelled from your center to move.

VI. Try Easy!

I am indebted to Al Chung-liang Huang for the inspiration for this movement for mending. A t'ai chi master, Al is also a master at getting people to move with the quality of the *chi* (life force) without getting hung up in a perfectionism of doing the form correctly. The spirit of the ancient art of t'ai chi is to playfully practice moving with a "try easy" spirit, challenging oneself to let go of any unnecessary tension. Try easy to make each movement as effortless and pleasurable as possible.

1. Stand with feet separated at least the width of your own shoulders.
2. Balance equally on both feet so that your body is positioned in the center of the space between your feet.
3. Soften your knees so that they bend slightly. (Remember, your knees are your shock absorbers and, when locked, they cannot operate for this purpose.)
4. Gently move the trunk of your body to the right and in a slightly curved angle, shifting your weight so that it rests on your right foot.
5. Move the trunk of your body gently in the reverse direction, through the center and to the left, so that your weight is on your left foot. The path you are traveling is like a C turned on its side.
6. Repeat these movements, making sure that you are breathing to accompany the movement.
7. Now add movements of your arms and hands so that they accompany the rest of your movements. As your arms move inward toward the center, inhale. As your arms move outward, exhale.
8. Experiment with different arm movements, coordinating your hands and arms so they are together in front of your body when

your weight is in the center. Allow your arms to move out into space as you shift your weight to one foot or the other.

9. The quality of your movement should be like the graceful slow motion replay of televised sporting events. Some people use the image of moving through clouds, or moving in a weightless environment such as a spaceship, or swimming underwater like scuba divers.

10. Continue these movements for two to three minutes, allowing the movement to change as you explore moving as effortlessly as possible.

11. As you are moving, notice any places in your body where you begin to have discomfort or tiredness. Imagine sending your breath to these places so that you can let go of any excess tension you are carrying.

EXTRA BONUS:

12. After you are comfortable with this type of movement, add a message that you would love to believe deep in your soul. Repeat the expression as you perform the movements. Examples: "I am relaxing in the arms of the unfolding universe." "The world is unfolding in exactly the right way." "I am a valuable and precious person."

VII. Boundary Builder

Caregivers need to be careful not to take in the toxic energy of complaining clients, hostile staff, blaming bosses, or pleading family members. One way to take care of ourselves is to boost our boundary system and practice building boundaries of protection.

1. Rub palms of your hands together.
2. Keeping palms facing each other, separate them slightly. Begin moving palms in relationship to each other until you can feel

the energy or sense the space between them. (Some people experience temperature change or a sense of density in the space between their hands.)

3. With your hands, begin tracing an imaginary boundary for yourself in space, several inches from your body. You can strengthen this boundary by imaging a color and consistency of material. Remember that this boundary needs to be semipermeable to allow positive energy to enter and negative energy to leave.

4. Turn your palms outward and move this "space capsule" you have created so that it can expand as you stretch out in different directions. Make certain that you can move freely inside the area that you have defined for yourself.

5. Explore any place where your protective membrane may need extra fortification (perhaps in front of your heart, or behind your back, or behind your knees). Fortify these more vulnerable places by imagining a thicker membrane around them. Imagine sending your breath to these places as you move.

REAL LIFE APPLICATION

When you find yourself feeling drained in the presence of a particular person, remember this activity and imagine doing it in your mind's eye. Later, if you must deal with the person again, you may perform the entire movement series immediately prior to coming into their presence.

VIII. Moving Out: A Drawing Becomes a Moving Picture

Physical and emotional pain occurs when we unconsciously hold tension in our bodies. Try this remedy for discovering how and where you are holding tension and for experimenting with getting the energy to move on out. Anna Halprin calls this type of process "psychokinetic visualization." For this activity you will need to have some art supplies handy. Prepare to have a large newsprint pad and crayons or colored marking pens nearby.

1. After completing one of the exercises above or some other physical activity, lie down on the floor on your back.

2. Closing your eyes, imagine that you can send your awareness, like a searchlight, through the inside of your body.

3. Begin at the top of your head and travel down your body, sensing behind your eyes, inside your nose, inside your mouth. (If you have trouble doing this, swallow, and you will feel the inside of your throat.)

4. After you have completed sensing your entire body down to your feet, send the searchlight back up through your torso to the top of your head.

5. Now imagine what your body would look like from the inside if you had a special camera that could view the inner terrain.

6. Sit up slowly, take art materials, and draw your body from what you have sensed from the inside. Use color and texture to highlight areas that stand out to you. Indicate areas that you are not able to feel from the inside.

7. Fasten your drawing to a wall where you can view it without having to hold it.

8. Become your drawing, assuming the posture and angles represented.

9. After you have gotten a feel of your drawing as a still image, allow yourself to move so that you (as your drawing) become a moving picture. Name your picture if a title occurs to you at this point.

10. Go back to the still position and see if there is some other way that this picture (and your body) could move.

11. Return to your position on the floor and notice whether your body feels any different from when you began.

12. Ask yourself, "What does this picture say about my life?"

APPENDIX B
Transformation of a Career: A Healing Ritual

The scene is a forested backyard. Folding chairs have been placed in rows facing a raised deck overlooking a small stream. Approximately 30 participants file into the backyard and are seated while the Shaker song "Tis a Gift to Be Simple" plays in the background. The presiding woman minister begins.

"Dearly beloved, we are gathered here in the sight of God, the university, the county, nation, and world to witness and participate in the transformation of the career and life work of this woman, Sheila Collins. Since all members present have had ample and sufficient opportunity to object to this transformation (committees having met, votes having been counted, petitions having been heard, pipes having been smoked, hands having been wrung, and floors having been paced), I hereby declare that all persons involved with this woman's career life must herein and after *forever hold their peace!*"

Reading

An excerpt from Jean Auel's *Clan of the Cave Bears* is read by Sheila's son, Kevin. Bringing in the archetypical element of shunning, Kevin reads of how Ayla, girl of the Clan, is banished for using a weapon (a slingshot), which is against the traditions of the Clan: "The clan didn't care if the spirit took the body with it, or left the unmoving shell behind, but they wanted the spirit of Ayla to go, and go quickly."

Distribution of the Elements

(A filing cabinet on a dolly is wheeled from the building at this point, accompanied by pallbearers, colleagues, and dignitaries from Sheila's past career life.) The minister continues: "It is important that we re-member that the contents of this cabinet though containing all of the original manuscripts written by Dr. Collins prior to and during her academic career, including articles (published, rejected, and under editorial consideration at this time), book chapters, course syllabi for both credit and noncredit courses, grant proposals (funded, rejected, and under editorial consideration at this time), and all memos and letters, carbons of memos and letters, and later, Xerox copies of memos and letters), are not as important as Dr. Sheila K. Collins herself. In spite of the breadth and depth of the material that we are about to throw into this fire, we must remember that the real abilities, gifts, visions, and spirit of their author remain ever with us. These items, though they represent thousands of hours of effort, dedication, discipline, uncooked meals, sleepless nights, and missed television programs—not to mention missed ski trips, missed sporting events, missed soap operas, and ladies' luncheons—these items do not represent the real creativity, artistry, scholarship, and acquired "street smarts" that the woman, Sheila K. Collins, has developed during this period of her career and life's work." (As the song "All My Life's a Circle" is played, the head pallbearer opens the first drawer of the file cabinet and distributes the contents to individuals in the audience.)

Testimonials

When all the manila folders have been distributed, the minister says, "We now take time to share our reflections, feelings, visions, and versions of Sheila K. Collins's work life." Friends, colleagues, former students, and family members remember aloud aspects of Sheila's career life. Mention is made of her free spirit and creativity and of her tendency to be "ahead of her time."

Elevation

The minister directs the congregation: "Please stand, raise your manila folders and envelopes to the heavens, and repeat after me: "We offer these gifts to the Great Mother as evidence of our faith in the strength of her spirit, that same spirit which is reflected in these writings and other creative expressions of author Sheila K. Collins.

"In spite of the lack of evidence of appreciation, reward, recognition, monetary compensation, the granting of tenure, or the real and authentic opportunity to earn same, we hereby affirm our belief that the Great Mother will see to the success and fulfillment of all those who have attempted to serve her. We affirm our belief that the Great Mother will insist that these offerings of Dr. Collins and those of her courageous coauthors and collaborators will not be burned in vain. Neither will she set in motion a vengeful spirit, since she alone fully appreciates the progress that has been made since ancestral sisters were personally burned at other stakes of institutional righteousness. Amen.

"Praise God and prepare to fuel the fire."

Reading

Sheila's husband, Richard, selects and reads the story of the origin of the pipe from *Black Elk Speaks*. He tells of two scouts seeing a woman approaching, and how one of them was foolish and had bad thoughts of the woman. When he approached her, a cloud came and covered them, and when the cloud was gone, the man was a skeleton covered with worms. The story continues as the woman goes into a teepee singing:

> *"With visible breath I am walking.*
> *A voice I am sending as I walk,*
> *In a sacred manner I am walking,*
> *With visible tracks I am walking.*
> *In a sacred manner I walk."*

Offering

People in the congregation begin a procession around an incinerator, and each person, in turn, throws the folder he or she is holding into the fire. The song "It's in Every One of Us" plays in the background. Meanwhile, a singer chants in a minor key the curriculum vitae of Dr. Collins, gradually increasing the tempo until a drummer joins in, syncopating the rhythm. The congregation snaps fingers to the beat.

Reading

A passage from the poem *Burnt Norton*, by T.S. Eliot, is read by Sheila's son, Ken.

IMPROVISATION/TRANSFORMATION

The song "Lord of the Dance" is sung by Sheila's daughter, Corinne, in accompaniment to her mother's improvisational dance.

Celebration

As the solo dance ends, Sheila leads the ritual participants in a community dance, which is accompanied by "The Song of the Soul." A reception follows the ceremony.

REFERENCES

Auel, Jean M., *The Clan of the Cave Bear* (Bantam Books: New York, 1985), p.271.
Neihardt, John G., *Black Elk Speaks* (University of Nebraska Press: Lincoln, Nebraska, 1981), p.5.

APPENDIX C
A Special Resource

After sending a written request for permission to use a few lines from the song "Let There Be Peace on Earth," I received a phone call from Jill Jackson Miller, the woman who, with her husband, wrote the song in 1955. After finding out more about the book I was writing, Ms. Miller generously suggested that I include all the words to her song. As she told me some of the stories about the song and how it has been used throughout the years, we both agreed it was a valuable resource for the readers of this book. It is offered here as a gift from the song's author, who believes as I do, that caregivers must take care of themselves as well as taking care of others.

Let there be peace on earth,

And let it begin with me.

Let there be peace on earth.

The peace that was meant to be.

*With God our creator,

Children all are we.

Let us walk with each other

in perfect harmony.

Let peace begin with me.

Let this be the moment now.

With every step I take

Let this be my solemn vow,

To take each moment and

Live each moment in peace eternally.

Let there be peace on earth

And let it begin with me.

*(Original, "With God as our father / Brothers all are we. / Let me walk with my brother , , ,")

APPENDIX D
Body-Oriented Resources

A major theme of this book has been that taking care of oneself involves taking care of one's body. Attending to the needs of the physical body provides access and benefit to the mental, emotional, and spiritual dimensions of the self as well. Throughout this book references have been made to "bodywork," "movement work," and "body-oriented psychotherapy." The following resource guide is offered to assist you in selecting the methods and systems that are right for you in particular phases of your self-caring, self-healing journey.

Physical

All bodywork systems deal with the physical body, but the ones listed below focus primarily on structure, alignment, posture, and the mechanical functioning of the body.

Massage Therapy – Most people's view of what constitutes massage is much narrower than the repertoire of a well-trained and experienced massage therapist. Swedish message, which involves long, smooth strokes for a sense of connection between areas of the body and light strokes to facilitate relaxation, fits most people's view of massage. Sports massage, a deep tissue massage to relieve sore muscles, is another popular style. But experienced massage therapists are likely to include many techniques in their work, developing their own synthesis of styles, perhaps including some of the techniques listed below. Contact American Massage Therapy Association, https://www.amtamassage.org/.

Alexander Technique – Named after its founder, F. M. Alexander, an Australian actor, this system aims to assist people in changing the way they use themselves physically as they perform everyday tasks. Alexander teachers work one-on-one with students, offering suggestions primarily through gentle touch and minimal verbal instruction.

The technique seeks to reduce effort, restore neuromuscular balance, and increase self-awareness. The method is well known in England. John Dewey and Aldous Huxley were enthusiastic supporters. Alexander Technique, https://www.alexandertechnique.com/.

Feldenkrais Method – Developed by Israeli physicist Moshe Feldenkrais, this work has two components: Awareness Through Movement (a form of exercise done slowly in groups) and Functional Integration (a practitioner does hands-on, gentle manipulation that increases awareness while inhibiting habitual movement patterns). Feldenkrais Method, https://www.feldenkrais.com/.

Rolfing – Named after founder Ida Rolf, this system involves a series of 10 sessions of deep tissue manipulation, each involving different areas of the body. The goal is to free the body from chronic tension for increased range of motion and improved posture. Rolfing, https://rolf.org/.

Chiropractic – The doctor of chiropractic specializes in the neurological and structural relationships of the body and their effects on health and disease. Hands-on manipulation is used to realign the body and to allow organs to function properly. Chiropractic, https://www.acatoday.org/.

Osteopathy – Osteopathic physicians are medical doctors, many of whom perform a gentle hands-on manipulative treatment to align the body and assist its recuperative system. One practitioner, John Upledger, has taken this work further and has trained massage therapists, physical therapists, and others to use his method, CranioSacral Therapy. One aspect, which he calls Somato-Emotional Release, deals with the emotional connections to physical imbalances. Contact Upledger Institute, https://www.upledger.com/. For osteopathy, www.osteopathic.org/.

Acupuncture or Acupressure (Shiatsu) – Acupuncture is the technique (from Chinese medicine) of inserting fine metal needles into the skin to treat ailments and relieve pain. Acupressure uses the same 100 to 150 pressure points but substitutes finger pressure for the needles. These methods can be used for prevention of illness and to aid in childbirth and surgery. Contact Acupuncture, http://www.acupuncture.com/; acupressure (shiatsu), http://acupressure.com/.

Emotional

Some bodywork systems engage in physical activities or movements primarily to evoke an emotional response. When a person expresses the unexpressed, the energy she or he has been using to inhibit emotions is freed for more productive endeavors.

Reichian – Wilhelm Reich, a student of Freud's, placed the body in a central role in personality theory. He developed a technique to mobilize feelings through breathing and hands-on contact and pressure aimed at dissolving what he called "character armour" in the body. One of the most direct-line developments from Reich's work in this country is **Bioenergetics Therapy.** Designed by Alexander Lowen, this system engages clients in breathing activities and postures that stress the body to the point of emotional release. This system emphasizes the importance of sexual expression and release. The practitioner assists the client in connecting the physical tension and emotional release with the issues and situations from the person's past and present life experience. Contact http://reichianinstitute.org/therapy.htm.

Lomi Bodywork – A connective tissue therapy and psychotherapy, Lomi was created by a physician, Robert Hall, and Richard Heckler, a psychologist, in the early 70s. Gestalt therapy is a part of the verbal aspect of this integrative approach, along with hands-on touch. The practitioner directs the clients' attention to muscular tension so they can discover how they are and who they are. Contact Bioenergetics

Therapy – Southern California Institute for Bioenergetic Analysis, http://sciba.org/.

Mental (Integrative)

The systems in this section are integrative, using the body to access physical, mental, emotional, and spiritual aspects of the person and to assist the person in integrating these dimensions of the self.

Rubenfeld Synergy Method – Developed by Ilana Rubenfeld, this method is a synthesis of gestalt therapy, Feldenkrais, and Alexander work to which imagery, hypnosis, and the use of humor have been added. Through gentle touch and movement, clients are encouraged to discover the connection between their physical tensions and the issues and feelings of their past and present life. Contact www.rubenfeldsynergy.com.

InterPlay – Developed by dancing ministers Cynthia Winton Henry and Phil Porter in California in the late 80s, this art-based system has become a social movement with practitioners in 50 sites and on 5 continents. This active, creative approach to unlocking the wisdom of the body taps movement, voice, stillness, and stories—our birthright practices—to help people of all ages connect to themselves and with one another. Interplay, www.interplay.org.

Hellerwork – Developed by Joseph Heller, a former Rolfer, this method consists of at least 10 sessions, working on movement of the structure of the body to restore natural balance. The client is encouraged to explore the feelings and images that arise as the practitioner works with the deep tissues of the body. See http://www.josephheller.com/whatis.html.

Hakomi Method – Developed by Ron Kurtz, Hakomi is a body-centered psychotherapy that works with the principles of nonviolence and mindfulness. The practitioner approaches the client with gentle respect and supports the person's accessing of core memories. By physically taking over the client's chronic holding patterns, the client is given the opportunity to let go of the tension and experience whatever feelings or memories the holding is connected to. Pat Ogden, with Ron Kurtz, has developed a table work or hands-on version of Hakomi that includes verbal instruction. See http://hakomiinstitute.com/about/the-hakomi-method.

Movement and Expressive Arts Therapy – This integrative way of working with dance, drama, visual arts, and music was developed by Anna Halprin and her associates at Tamalpa Institute. A psychokinetic visualization process is used to move back and forth between movement, felt sensation, imagery, and symbols and drawing. Core material is often generated, explored, and expressed. The work, now continued by Anna's daughter Daria Halprin, goes beyond therapy of the individual to include a collective creativity process and community transformation through events such as the annual Circle the Earth Peace Ritual. Contact Tamalpa Institute, http://www.tamalpa.org/.

SomaticExpression – Jamie McHugh, a dancer and nature photographer, has developed this integrative approach to the art and craft of embodiment over the past 35 years. The system is informed by movement traditions centered on body wisdom, most notably Body-Mind Centering®, Continuum, and Tamalpa Life/Art Process. The intention of Somatic Expression is to use these techniques to re-wild the body, mend the mind, and invite nature back into our modern lives.

Trager Work – Designed by physician Milton Trager, this work consists of a systematic set of gentle shaking, stretching, and rocking movements done while the person is lying on a table. The aim is to assist the client in letting go of tension and in releasing and lengthening. Imagery and meditation are also used. There is also a dance form (Mentastics) abstracted from the table work that is used to maintain the balance gained. Contact United States Trager Institute, https://www.tragerus.org/.

Spiritual

Methods and traditions that use movement to attain a higher consciousness are listed here. These bodywork traditions often use the concept of energy as in the chakras, or energy centers. Practitioners of these methods may consider themselves to be transferring healing energy from themselves to another or altering their own body/ mind state to a state of oneness with all. Yoga, shamanism, and faith healing would fall into this category of bodywork.

Therapeutic Touch – Developed by a nurse, Dolores Krieger, this system has been taught to nurses and other health professionals around the United States. Practitioners place themselves in a meditative state but do not actually touch the patient. They touch only the energy field or aura around the person in order to stimulate the recuperative powers of the patient. For more information on Therapeutic Touch, see http://therapeutictouch.org/.

Tai Chi – The oldest of the martial arts, this movement activity is called a "moving meditation." A person, alone or simultaneously with others, moves as effortlessly as possible through positions or postures, expressing the notion that change is the only constant in the universe. American Tai Chi and Qigong Association, http://www.americantaichi.org/.

Polarity Therapy – Developed by Dr. Randolf Stone, this system involves manipulation, exercise, diet, love, and thought to promote relaxation and help maintain normal body functioning. American Polarity Therapy Association, https://polaritytherapy.org/.

Yoga – There are many ancient and modern schools of yoga (https://www.yogaalliance.org/), but one resource that fits the self-care and self-healing theme of this book is the work of Eleanor Criswell Hanna. A professor of psychology, she is involved in yoga and the field of bio-feedback. Dr. Hanna has worked closely with her late husband, Thomas Hanna, in the development of the field of Somatics. She continues a journal by that name and a research institute, http://www.somaticsed. com/novinstitute.html. Also contact Novato Institute, 1516 Grant Ave., Suite 212, Novato, CA 94945, USA.

Notes

PROLOGUE

1. R. D. Laing, *The Politics of the Family* (New York: Vintage Books, Random House, 1969), p.31.
2. Christina Maslach, *Burnout: The Cost of Caring* (Englewood Cliffs, NJ: Prentice-Hall, 1982).
3. Compassion fatigue: Between 16% and 85% of health care workers in various fields develop compassion fatigue. In one study, approximately 85% of emergency room nurses met the criteria for compassion fatigue. In another study, more than 25% of ambulance paramedics were identified as having severe ranges of post-traumatic symptoms. In addition, 34% of hospice nurses in another study met the criteria for secondary traumatic stress /compassion fatigue. See M. Van Mol, E. Kompanje, J. Bakker, and M. Nijkamp, "Compassion Fatigue and Burnout among Healthcare Professionals in the ICU," *Critical Care* (2014):19.
4. For more about the status of women's work, see Anne Statham, Eleanor Miller, and Hans Maukschc, eds., *The Worth of Women's Work: A Qualitative Synthesis* (Albany, NY: State University of New York Press, 1988).
5. Linda Esposito, "6 Signs of a Codependent Relationship," https://www.psychologytoday.com/us/blog/anxiety-zen/201609/6-signs-codependent-relationship/ (accessed May 9, 2018).
6. For an excellent examination and delineation of a caring ethic, see Nell Noddings, *Caring: A Feminine Approach to Ethics and Moral Education* (Berkeley, CA: University of California Press, 1984).
7. Hans Selye, *The Stress of Life* (New York: McGraw Hill, 1978) and *Stress Without Distress* (Philadelphia: Lippincott Williams & Wilkins, 1974).
8. InterPlay, http://www.interplay.org./
9. Bernie Siegye, *Love, Medicine and Miracles* (New York: Harper and Row, 1986).
10. F. M. Alexander, *The Use of the Self* (New York: E. P. Dutton, 1932. Centerline Press edition, Downey, California, 1984).

251

11. Moshe Feldenkrais, *Awareness Through Movement* (New York: Harper and Row, 1972, 1977).
12. Ilana Rubenfeld, "Beginner's Hands: Twenty-five Years of Simple," *Somatics* (Spring/Summer 1988):4–11.
13. See "What is EMDR?" http://www.emdr.com/what-is-emdr/ (accessed May 9, 2018).
14. Nick Ortner, "What Is Tapping and How Can I Start Using It?" https://www.thetappingsolution.com/what-is-eft-tapping/ (accessed May 9, 2018).

OVERTURE, REVISED SECOND EDITION

1. Family Caregiver Alliance, "Caregiver Statistics: Demographics," https://www.caregiver.org/caregiver-statistics-demographics/ (accessed April 2, 2018).
2. American Psychology Association, "The High Costs of Caregiving," http://www.apa.org/research/action/caregiving.aspx/ (accessed April 2, 2018).
3. Gary Morse, Michelle P. Salyers, Angela L. Rollins, Maria Monroe-DeVita, and Corey Pfahler, "Burnout in Mental Health Services: A Review of the Problem and Its Remediation," *Adm Policy Mental Health* (2012): 1–2.
4. Patricia Cohen, "Working, but Needing Public Assistance Anyway," https://www.nytimes.com/2015/04/13/business/economy/working-but-needing-public-assistance-anyway.html/ (accessed April 3, 2018).
5. Sheila K. Collins, *Warrior Mother: Fierce Love, Unbearable Loss and Rituals that Heal* (Berkeley, CA: She Writes Press, 2013).
6. InterPlay, http://www. InterPlay.org/.
7. Kristin Neff, http://self-compassion.org/mindful-self-compassion-workbook/.
8. There are hundreds of books on the topic, but I'll offer the one my husband, Richard Citrin, coauthored with Allen Weiss, *The Resilient Advantage: Stop Managing Stress and Find your Resilience* (New York: Business Expert Press, 2016).

CHAPTER 1

1. *Soma* is a Greek word meaning "living body" and refers to the self-sensing, internalized perception of oneself from the inside. See Thomas Hanna, *The Body of Life* (New York: Knopf, 1980) or the same author's *Somatics* (Boston: Addison-Wesley Publishing, 1988), pp.5–7.
2. In spite of the Bible's positive reference to dancing (Psalm 150, "Praise the Lord with your dancing!"), some Christian churches continue to forbid dancing as sinful.
3. Timothy Leary and others began experimenting with drugs as a way to alter consciousness and learn more about how the mind works.
4. I am indebted to Ilana Rubenfeld for the notion of using the image of brackets to prevent past events from contaminating present interactions.

5. For an expanded definition of a partnership model that involves linking with others rather than dominating them, see Riane Eisler, *The Chalice and the Blade* (San Francisco: Harper and Row, 1987) and online, http://rianeeisler.com/partnership-101/.

CHAPTER 2

1. This prayer was written by Reinhold Niebuhr and later made popular by members of Alcoholics Anonymous and other twelve step self-help groups.
2. Family Caregiver Alliance, "Caregiver Statistics: Demographics," https://www.caregiver.org/caregiver-statistics-demographics/ (accessed April 2, 2018).

CHAPTER 3

1. Poems were written by Ralph Caplan for Herman Miller Corporation's ad campaign to introduce modular office systems. Used with permission.
2. For more about the way interior design impacts our behavior, see Ralph Caplan, *By Design* (New York: St. Martin's Press, 1982).
3. David Sturt and Todd Nordstrom, "Is Sitting the New Smoking?" https://www.forbes.com/sites/davidsturt/2015/01/13/is-sitting-the-new-smoking/#11b88d834fd4/ (accessed April 1, 2018).
4. I am especially indebted to the designer Louis Nelson for his discussion with me regarding the importance of lighting in the workplace. See also Carol Venolia, *Healing Environments* (Berkley, CA: Celestial Arts. 1988).
5. Laurier Wilfrid, "Using Music During Childbirth," *Birth* 27, no. 4 (Dec. 2000):272–6.
6. This Celebration Policy was found years ago and the source is unknown. It hung on the wall of Iatria.

CHAPTER 4

1. Title IX, the federal enabling legislation of 1972, states, "No person on the basis of sex shall be excluded from participation in, or subject to discrimination under any educational program or activity receiving federal financial assistance."
2. Consultation to school districts took place under auspices of the Center for Co-Equal Education, University of Nebraska, Lincoln, funded by the US Office of Health, Education and Welfare.
3. Examples of the slowness of the wheels of justice include the fifty-plus years it has taken for reparation checks to be sent to the survivors and heirs of the Japanese American citizens incarcerated in camps during World War II. Closer to home, personally, is the class action salary discrimination suit I was a part of, filed in 1974 and never settled, on behalf of women employees at the University of Nebraska.

4. There is no longer a separate listing for Codependents Anonymous for Helping Professionals. Their former address was CODAHP, Box 42253, Mesa, AZ 85274–2253.

CHAPTER 5

1. This technique was inspired by R. D. Laing's *Knots* (New York: Random House, 1972).
2. For more information about the Rubenfeld Synergy Method, visit the website, https://www.rubenfeldsynergy.com/.
3. The programmed messages referred to here have been identified in the system of Transactional Analysis as the most common drivers (motivators that "drive" a person to behave in certain ways). According to this theory, messages from childhood interfere with a person's ability to be inner-directed and supersede the person's meeting his or her own needs.

CHAPTER 6

1. Deane Juhan, *Job's Body* (Barrytown, NY: Station Hill Press, 1987), p.19.
2. Appreciation to Dan Millman for the five aspects of physical fitness. See Dan Millman, *The Warrior Athlete: Body, Mind, and Spirit* (Walpole, NH: Stillpoint, 1985).
3. Workshop leader in this example was Ilana Rubenfeld, who is also an Alexander teacher.
4. C. H. Stevens, "The Development of the Alexander Technique and Evidence for Its Effects," *British Journal of Therapy and Rehabilitation* 2, no. 11 (1997):621–626.
5. Julian Silverman, *Health Care and Consciousness* (New York: Irvington Publishers, 1983).
6. Juhan, *Job's Body* (see note 1 above), p.xxix.
7. For a discussion of the anatomy of stress, see Phil Nuernberger, *Freedom from Stress* (Honesdale, PA: Himalayan International Institute, 1981), ch. 2, pp. 35–74.

CHAPTER 7

1. Ernest Rossi, *The Psychobiology of Mind-Body Healing* (New York: W.W. Norton, 1986).
2. Karl H. Pribram, "Holonomy and Structure in the Organization of Perception," http://www.karlpribram.com/wp-content/uploads/pdf/theory/T-095.pdf/ (accessed March 2, 2018).
3. Sidran Institute, https://www.sidran.org/resources/for-survivors-and-loved-ones/post-traumatic-stress-disorder-fact-sheet-2/ (accessed April 20, 2018).

4. Katheryn J. Lively, "Affirmations: The Why, What, How, and What If?" https://www.psychologytoday.com/us/blog/smart-relationships/201403/affirmations-the-why-what-how-and-what-if/ (accessed May 2, 2018).
5. Bernie Siegel, http://berniesiegelmd.com/.
6. Jeanne Achterberg, *Imagery In Healing* (Boston: Shambhala, 1985).
7. Barry Stevens, *Don't Push the River: It Flows by Itself* (Berkeley, CA: Celestial Arts, 1970) and Gendlin, Eugene, *Focusing* (New York: Bantam Books, 1981).
8. Jamie McHugh, "An Introduction to Embodied Mindfulness," http://www.somaticexpression.com/articles/documents IntroductiontoEmbodiedMindfulness.pdf / (accessed April 2, 2018).
9. Ibid.
10. Jon Kabat-Zinn, *Wherever You Go, There You Are: Mindfulness Meditation in Everyday Life* (New York: Hatchette Books, 2005).
11. L. N. Dyrbye, T.D. Shanafelt, C.A. Sinsky, P.F. Cipriano, J. Bhatt, A. Ommaya, C.P. West, and D. Meyers, 2017. "Burnout among Health Care Professionals: A call to Explore and Address This Underrecognized Threat to Safe, High-Quality Care." NAM Perspectives. Discussion Paper, National Academy of Medicine, Washington, DC, https://nam.edu/Burnout-Among-Health-Care-Professionals (accessed 3/21/2018).

CHAPTER 8

1. Deane Juhan, *Job's Body* (see note 1 in ch. 6, above) p. xxviii.
2. John Fox, http://www.poeticmedicine.org/.
3. Interplay, http://www.interplay.org/.
4. Paul Pearsall, *Super Immunity* (New York: McGraw Hill, 1987).

CHAPTER 9

1. Leo Booth, *Spirituality and Recovery* (Pompano Beach, FL: Health Communications, 1985), p. 4.
2. Barry Stevens, *Don't Push the River: It Flows by Itself* (Highlands, NY: Gestalt Journal Press, 2005).
3. T. S. Eliot, "Burnt Norton," in *Complete Poems and Plays, 1909–1950* (San Diego, CA: Harcourt Brace Jovanovich, 1950, 1980), p. 119. Used with permission.
4. American Dance Therapy Association. *Marian Chace: Dancer & Pioneer Dance Therapist*, https://adta.org/marian-chace-biography/ (accessed 5/8/18).
5. Marilyn Doucet and Martin Rovers, "Generational Trauma, Attachment, and Spiritual/Religious Interventions," *Journal of Loss and Trauma*, 15, no. 2 (2010):93–105.
6. Phil Porter, *Having It All: Body, Mind, Heart & Spirit Together Again* (Oakland, CA: Wing It! Press, 1997), p. 69.

7. Cynthia Winton-Henry, *What the Body Wants* (Oakland, CA: Wood Lake Publishing, 2004).
8. Glenda Taylor, http://www.oneandallwisdom.com/ (accessed April 4, 2018).
9. Brené Brown, https://www.brenebrown.com/ (accessed Feb 14, 2018).
10. Cynthia Phelps, https://www.cynthiaphelps.com/ (accessed Jan 9, 2018).

CHAPTER 10

1. Musical resources for family rituals include Beethoven's "Consecration of the House Overture, Opus 124," and the folk song "Bless This House."

Index

257

AFFIRMATIONS

EXERCISES

POEMS

About the Authors

Sheila K. Collins, PhD, has referred to herself as a "dancing social worker" for over 40 years. Bringing the perspective of a theater artist to her work as a social worker, professor, clinic director, keynote speaker, and organizational consultant, she writes, speaks, and advocates for the power of play, dance, and the expressive arts to help us make it through life's toughest challenges.

Stillpoint was written originally to help social work students with their self-care, and the revision as a response to the proliferation of caregiving responsibilities in women's lives. Her award-winning book, *Warrior Mother: Fierce Love, Unbearable Loss and the Rituals that Heal,* tells of her journeys with two of her three adult children and her best friend through their life-threatening illnesses and deaths and of the rituals that helped her family to heal.

Her engaging 2016 TEDx talk, *"When Death Threatens,"* demonstrates the challenge and the gifts of being a caregiver to a loved one dealing with a death-defying illness. Sheila holds an MSW from Wayne State University School of Social Work and a PhD from the University of Nebraska at Lincoln. She currently directs and performs with the *Wing & A Prayer Pittsburgh Players* and writes a weekly blog, *Dancing with Everything,* on her website, www.sheilakcollins.com.

Christine Gautreaux, MSW, is the helpers' helper. Through individual coaching, collaborative workshops, and women's retreats she helps women maintain self-care, manifest their dreams, and learn artful ways to make a difference in the world. Christine's social justice work includes teaching the tools of InterPlay to incarcerated women and people living with severe and persistent mental illness and homelessness.

Christine holds an MSW from the University of Houston, Texas, with a specialty in clinical services, and a bachelor's degree from Stephen F. Austin State University, Nacogdoches, Texas. She performs as a founding member of the improvisational InterPlay-based performance company *SoulPrint Players* in Atlanta. She enjoys traveling with her friend Sheila and they'd love to come meet you and present and perform in your community. Her website is at https://www.christine-gautreaux.com/.